# THE BASICS

# Business Communication

## Patricia Merrier

University of Minnesota Duluth
Duluth, Minnesota

VISIT US ON THE INTERNET
# www.swep.com
www.thomsonlearning.com

**South-Western**
EDUCATIONAL PUBLISHING
Thomson Learning™

Australia • Canada • Denmark • Japan • Mexico • New Zealand • Philippines
Puerto Rico • Singapore • South Africa • Spain • United Kingdom • United States

Business Unit Director:   Peter McBride
Executive Editor:   Eve Lewis
Project Manager:   Penny Shank
Editor:   Alan Biondi
Production Manager:   Patricia Matthews Boies
Art/Design Coordinator:   Bill Spencer
Marketing Manager:   Mark Linton
Cover Design:   Lou Ann Thesing
Manufacturing Coordinator:   Pam Wulf
Compositor:   Better Graphics, Inc.

ISBN: 0-538-72295-9

3 4 5 6 7 8 9 0   MZ   06 05 04 03 02

Printed in the United States of America

For permission to use material from this text or product, contact us by
* web: www.thomsonrights.com
* Phone: 1-800-730-2214
* Fax: 1-800-730-2215

# CONTENTS

# PREFACE

You are about to explore a critical and exciting area of your business program. Clear, accurate, timely written communication is critical to the success of business and important to your success *in* business.

## ORGANIZATION

*Basics of Business Communication* is designed to help you refine your writing skills and adapt them to business situations. The text-workbook contains seven chapters:

- Chapter 1 introduces you to the communication process, including the characteristics of business messages and the barriers that interfere with effective communication.
- Chapter 2 takes you through the mental and physical processes of planning business messages.
- Chapter 3 discusses the 4Cs of business communication and their importance in business writing.
- Chapters 4 through 6 present and let you apply the strategies used when writing positive, neutral, negative, and persuasive messages.
- Chapter 7 addresses the process of preparing an application letter and resume; it also discusses special business messages.

## SPECIAL FEATURES

*Basics of Business Communication* is more than a textbook.  It is a practical, results-oriented tool with the following features designed to help you write effective business messages:

- *Checkpoints* throughout the text challenge you to know *what* items to include in a message as well as *why* and *how* to include them.
- *Checkpoint solutions*, provided at the end of the book, let you verify your understanding of one section before you begin another section.
- *Examples* clarify and  reinforce chapter concepts.
- *Message-writing activities* cover both business and personal-business situations.
- *Margin notes and quotations* help you learn and recall important concepts.
- *Workplace Connections* provide realism and offer tips for succeeding on the job.
- *E-mail and Internet* activities help you develop online research skills.
- *Anecdotes and cartoons* add realism and humor to your study of business communication.
- *Chapter summaries* reinforce the principles covered in each chapter.
- *Chapter applications* put what you have learned to work by using your critical thinking, composition, proofreading, and teamwork skills.
- *Web- and CD ROM-based supplemental resources* provide current and timely research and application practice.
- *Appendixes* provide information about letter and memo formats, ZIP Code abbreviations, editing symbols, and frequently misused/confused words.

## ICONS

*Basics of Business Communication* uses icons to quickly identify some of its special features.

 The team icon identifies opportunities to work with others and sharpen your teamwork skills.

 The workplace connection icon identifies workplace success tips as well as information and exercises that reinforce the foundation skills and personal qualities employers look for when hiring.

 The Internet/e-mail icon marks activities where you may practice your online computer skills.

 The *words@work* icon alerts you to specific lessons and exercises from the *words@work* CD-ROM that correlate with each chapter. *Words@work* can be ordered separately from South-Western Educational Publishing/ Thomson Learning.

## THE SERIES

*Basics of Business Communication* may be used as a standalone resource or in conjunction with the **Basics of Communication Series**, a series of text-workbooks that helps you master the communication skills needed in the workplace. The other books in the series are *Basics of English, Basics of Writing, Basics of Employment Communication,* and *Basics of Speech Communication.*

## ACKNOWLEDGMENTS

Thanks are extended to the following individuals for reviewing the manuscript and for offering suggestions:

**Steven Griffin,** Consultant, El Paso, TX

**Kim Klorer,** University of Texas at El Paso, El Paso, TX

**Susan Merrill,** Educational Consultant, Croton-on-Hudson, NY

**Katherine Ploeger,** California State University Stanislaus, Turlock, CA

**Laurie Shapero,** Miami-Dade Community College, Kendall Campus, Miami, FL

This text acquaints you with the principles and processes necessary to communicate well. With study and practice, YOU can write effective business messages. Enjoy your study. Work hard. Succeed.

*Pat Merrier*

# UNDERSTANDING THE COMMUNICATION PROCESS

When employers are surveyed about the qualities they seek in potential employees, they consistently rate communication skills near the top. The results of one such survey were reported recently in *The Wall Street Journal* (12/19/98; page A1). The National Association of Colleges and

Employers surveyed 480 companies and public organizations and determined that ability to communicate ranked first among the qualities these employers look for in college graduates. Work experience was second, motivation third, and academic credentials sixth.

## COMMUNICATION IN THE WORKPLACE

Communication is the heart of every organization. Whether the organization is a family, a social or professional society, a not-for-profit entity, or a for-profit business, its members must interact—they must *communicate*. Good reading, writing, speaking, and listening skills are essential to accomplishing tasks and achieving goals.

"Wait," you say. "I've been communicating my whole life. What's different about this?"

The difference is that now you'll be focusing on *workplace* communication. You'll be asked to sharpen your skills and to apply them in new and different situations. Some of your communication efforts will be individual ones; others will be collaborative. In either case, you must perform them in a professional manner. Everything you do will be related to an objective or a goal. Your ability to communicate will mean success for you and your employer.

### LEARNING OBJECTIVES

- Be aware of the role communication plays in the workplace.
- Understand the communication process.
- Identify the characteristics of business messages.
- Recognize communication barriers and identify ways to minimize them.

*Employees and organizations need to communicate to succeed.*

## Why Communication Skills Are Important to You

You're enrolled in a post-secondary school program because you want to develop the skills to get a job and build a career. Communication is certainly one of those skills. As you work to build a successful career, you'll

*Effective communication will help you:*
- *Get a job*
- *Do your job*
- *Keep the job and earn promotions*

❝ **During the interview itself, I am highly sensitive to the relative strength or weakness of the individual's communication skills. It is essential for the candidate to be able to communicate clearly.** ❞

Elaine Swope, Director of Human Resources, Specialty Care Network

*Today's businesses face many challenges:*
- *Specialization*
- *Diversity*
- *Technology*

find that effective communication will be important to you in the following three ways:

1. You must communicate to get your job. You'll use your communication skills to prepare your application letter and résumé and to sell yourself during an interview.

2. You must communicate to do your job effectively. Regardless of the position you hold, you will interact with colleagues, clients, customers, and/or representatives of other organizations. Sharing data, preparing reports, collaborating on projects, and providing good customer service require effective, ethical communication.

3. You must communicate to advance in your career. Employers look for employees who can think and solve problems. In addition to performing the technical aspects of your job, you must be able to communicate your ideas for improving products and/or procedures. Showing you are interested in the long-term success of the organization will make you one of its valued and promoted members.

## Why Employers Look for Workers Who Communicate Well

You needn't look further than the classified ads in your local newspaper to know that employers want to hire people who have good communication skills. The ability to communicate effectively is listed as a desirable qualification in many classified ads. Why? The positive relationship between communication and organizational success is the primary reason. To be successful, organizations must respond to many challenges. As noted in the following list, some of those challenges involve communication.

1. The workplace is becoming more specialized. The trend toward specialization means that workers in different departments are less likely to understand one another's technical vocabulary. They must, therefore, exchange clearer and more complete messages.

2. The workplace is becoming more diverse. The global nature of business and a growing diversity in the domestic workforce mean that employees must consider the demographic characteristics of those with whom they communicate. Age, gender, disabilities, race/ethnicity, and nationality are among the factors to be recognized and respected.

3. The workplace is relying more on technology. Technology has affected the nature and speed of our communications. Workers must know how and when to use technology to help them communicate.

## CHECKPOINT 1-1

### VALUING COMMUNICATION

Why do you think communication skills rate higher than academic credentials (diplomas/degrees) in the survey results described in the Introduction to this chapter?

## The Focus of this Book

Although all types of communication are important in the workplace, this text will focus on written communication. You'll become acquainted with the kinds of written communication you can expect to use on the job. In addition, you'll learn and practice techniques designed to help you produce effective messages. Ready? Let's begin!

# COMMUNICATION CHARACTERISTICS

When asked to describe a friend or acquaintance, you will probably provide information about the person's physical characteristics—height, hair color, weight—and aspects of the person's character—honesty, loyalty, generosity. The same approach can be used when describing communication; the only difference is the terms used to describe the characteristics. *Mode*, *destination*, *flow*, and *style*, are among the terms used to describe the features of communication.

## Mode

Sometimes the **mode** (method) people use to communicate is words; sometimes it is actions. When communication is with words, its mode is **verbal**. Verbal communication may be spoken or written (do not confuse with oral communication, which is always spoken). Speeches, introductions, conversations, letters, memos, e-mail, and reports are examples of verbal communication. A communication's mode is **nonverbal** when it occurs through action or appearance. Handshakes, smiles, and frowns illustrate nonverbal communication that accompanies spoken messages. The format of a letter or report illustrates nonverbal communication associated with written messages.

> **❝ Accomplish-ments will prove to be a journey, not a destination. ❞**
>
> Dwight D. Eisenhower

*Verbal communication uses written or spoken words.*

## Destination

**Destination** refers to the target audience for the message. Business communication can be directed to *internal* or *external* receivers. **Internal** communication occurs when workers communicate with one another about the operation of their organization. A memorandum announcing a change in a personnel policy or an e-mail containing the agenda for a budget meeting are examples of internal communication. **External** communication occurs when employees send messages to people who do not belong to the organization. A letter to a customer explaining that an order has been delayed is an external communication.

## Flow

Communication can flow vertically, horizontally, or diagonally within the workplace.

VERTICAL COMMUNICATION. **Vertical communication** moves between individuals at different levels in an organization. Sometimes messages are sent from the CEO to all employees within an organization or from a vice president to all employees in his or her area only. Generally, though, vertical communication follows the "chain of command," the reporting lines reflected on an organizational chart. This means that a manager will send messages *downward* to those he or she supervises. Similarly, a worker will send a message *upward* to the person to whom he or she reports.

For organizations to be successful, the vertical lines of communication must be open. Employees want to know what is happening within their organization and why it is happening. Similarly, they want to know that their ideas and suggestions are welcomed and valued. Reports, announcements, newsletters, policy statements, and meetings all facilitate the kind of information exchange that keeps morale high and rumors and gossip to a minimum.

HORIZONTAL COMMUNICATION. **Horizontal communication** flows between or among peers (employees at the same level within an organization as reflected in the organizational chart). Messages that flow horizontally typically involve the exchange of data or information needed to accomplish routine tasks. The information can be shared through correspondence, during face-to-face conversations, or via telephone. The senders and receivers can be in the same department or in different units. The common bond is their need to cooperate.

DIAGONAL COMMUNICATION. **Diagonal communication** is exchanged between people who work in different units and at different levels within an organization. These messages facilitate the work of committees, teams, or task forces created to solve problems or complete projects.

---

*Written messages may be exchanged with people inside or outside the organization.*

*Messages can flow vertically, horizontally, or diagonally within an organization.*

WORKPLACE
CONNECTIONS

Teams are the norm in business today, and effective interpersonal communication (e.g., listening, speaking, conflict resolution, negotiating) are essential to both team membership and team leadership.

*Chapter 1: Understanding the Communication Process*

## Style

Regardless of their destination or flow, messages are sent in one of two styles—formal or informal. **Formal** communications use traditional formats. **Informal** communications are more free-flowing and relaxed. A formal written report, for example, will have a title page and a table of contents; an informal written report will have the title displayed on its first text page and will not contain a table of contents. Formal style does not require formal language. Business writing should be conversational and readable.

## Other Features

In addition to the features already described, business communications must be both ethical and legal. An **ethical message** meets the unwritten moral expectations of society. Meeting these standards is a matter of trust and integrity. When the expectations are not met, society's trust is violated and the violator's integrity is questioned. If repeated violations occur, society responds by enacting laws designed to enforce its ethical standards. Consumer protection laws, for example, were enacted to ensure fair treatment in interactions between buyers and sellers. A **legal message** meets the requirements of any laws (local, state, national, or international) that apply to its transaction.

## "We can do the job in one day for ten dollars. Oh. Wait a minute. I mean fifty days for ten million dollars."

The legal and ethical dimensions of communication can be challenging to monitor because of differences among governments, cultures, and individuals. Bribery and embezzlement illustrate those differences. In the United States, bribing a public official is illegal; in some other countries, the practice is expected. If a US business representative gives

*Formal messages have a more structured format than informal ones.*

*Be sure your messages are both ethical and legal.*

### WORKPLACE CONNECTIONS

Ethical standards vary by person, organization, and culture. Set high standards for yourself; maintain the high standards of your employer; recognize and respect differences among cultures.

money to a foreign official, has a law been violated? Ethics? Similarly, in the United States, it would be illegal for employees to embezzle money from their employers. Is it unethical, though, for a worker to use an organization's computer for personal activities such as preparing a paper for school? Some people would say yes; others, no. Employees have an obligation to know and adhere to the laws and codes of ethics that apply to their work.

## CHECKPOINT 1-2

### EXPLORING ETHICS

Some people believe the term "business ethics" is an oxymoron (contradictory term). Do you agree? Why or why not?

# THE WRITTEN COMMUNICATION PROCESS

*Communication is a process.*

Every written communication involves a **sender** and a **receiver**. The sender initiates the communication process by having an idea or some information to share with the receiver. The sender **encodes** (puts into words) and **transmits** (sends) the message via a **channel** (paper or electronic). The receiver then **decodes** (reads and interprets) the message and gives **feedback** to the sender. The process may be completed in one cycle, or it may be repeated several times. One cycle of the communication process is shown in Figure 1-1.

The communication process seems simple, almost perfect. When it succeeds, the sender and receiver achieve mutual understanding. In some cases, though, problems hamper or destroy the ability to attain this goal. These problems are called barriers. Effective communicators recognize potential barriers in the process and work to minimize or eliminate them.

# BARRIERS TO COMMUNICATION

*Barriers impede the communication process.*

Barriers can occur at any point in the communication process. The most common written communication barriers are described in the following paragraphs.

*Chapter 1: Understanding the Communication Process*

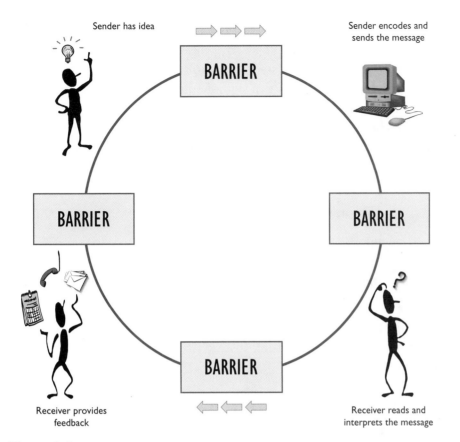

Sender has idea

Sender encodes and sends the message

BARRIER

BARRIER

BARRIER

BARRIER

Receiver provides feedback

Receiver reads and interprets the message

**Figure 1-1**
The Communication Process

## Poor Word Choice

The English language contains hundreds of thousands of words, and no person has command of them all. Instead, each individual develops two sets of vocabulary—a use vocabulary and a recognition vocabulary. The **use vocabulary** consists of words the individual regularly reads, hears, and/or writes. They are words one uses with confidence. The **recognition vocabulary** consists of words for which meaning can be derived from context. Word choice may become a barrier when the words the sender uses are not in the use or recognition vocabulary of the receiver. The relationship among user vocabulary, recognition vocabulary, and total words is shown in Figure 1-2.

*Poorly chosen words can be a barrier.*

*Choose specific, understandable words.*

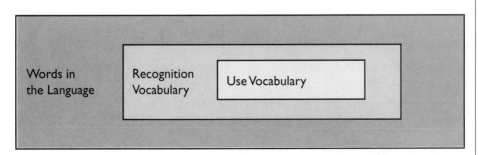

Words in the Language

Recognition Vocabulary

Use Vocabulary

**Figure 1-2**
Relationship Among Vocabulary Levels

Word choice typically arises as a barrier when senders write to "impress" rather than to "express" and when they rely too heavily on **jargon** (specialized, work-related terms) to convey their message. Possessing a large vocabulary is a sign of education; knowing when to use the words in that vocabulary is a measure of wisdom.

Word choice also can be a communication barrier when one uses connotative rather than denotative words. **Denotative** words are concrete and easily understood. **Connotative** words are *sense* based and, therefore, more vague. Examples of each follow:

| Denotative | Connotative |
|---|---|
| book | bright (compared to what?) |
| dozen | fast (compared to what?) |
| mile | few (compared to what?) |
| west | warm (compared to what?) |

For clarity, writers should use denotative words and phrases. Instead of "warm," give the temperature. Instead of "few," state how many out of a total, i.e., "12 of 3,000."

## Incorrect or Incomplete Content and Poor Organization

Messages must be accurate, complete, and well organized. Something as simple as using an incorrect day with a date causes confusion and generates the need for additional communication. If a message is incomplete, such as not listing the time for a meeting, more communication is needed. A poorly organized message also can be confusing. Saying that the receiver should "immediately [*do something*]" and then later saying "but not before you [*do something else*]" is confusing. Logical organization enhances written communication.

## Wrong Communication Channel

When a sender selects an inappropriate method to transmit a message, successful communication is jeopardized. Speed and the sender's relationship with the receiver are among factors to consider when selecting a communication channel. This topic will be covered in greater detail in Chapter 2.

## Grammar, Spelling, and Punctuation Errors

Errors in grammar, spelling, and punctuation not only impede understanding but also reflect poorly on writers and the organizations they represent. Imagine the embarrassment of the attorney who pointed toward a chart with the heading "Calender of Job Search Activity," or the chagrin of the federal office worker who accepted delivery of pens

> **"** Organizing is what you do before you do something, so that when you do it, it is not all mixed up. **"**
>
> A. A. Milne

*Content and organization are important to clear communication.*

*Transmission method can affect communication success.*

*Use language correctly.*

*Chapter 1: Understanding the Communication Process*

bearing the words "Untied States." Proofreading is essential, even when electronic resources such as spell check are used.

## Receiver Mistakes

Although the message sender has the heavy responsibility of removing communication barriers, the receiver also plays a role in good communication. The reader must give his or her full attention to the message and make a sincere effort to understand it. The receiver also has an obligation to provide verbal or nonverbal feedback. **Verbal feedback** includes acknowledgment, questions, and comments; **nonverbal feedback** includes facial expressions and body language. Unless the receiver takes this role seriously, he or she actually creates a communication barrier.

# WHY USE WRITTEN COMMUNICATION?

With all the potential obstacles to overcome, a sender might wonder why written communication is so common in the workplace. Written messages are popular because:

1. Written messages are long lasting. They can be filed for future reference. E-mail messages can be stored electronically or printed and stored in traditional files.

2. Written messages have legal value. Under certain conditions, letters and memos will be treated as contracts.

3. Written messages can be revised many times before they are sent. The writer can check to be sure the content is correct. Sentences can be rearranged; words can be changed. Electronic resources such as spell check and grammar check can be used as messages are drafted, revised, and edited.

4. Written messages can be read as many times as needed to understand their content. This is very important if a message is complex.

5. Written messages can be directed to many receivers at different locations.

6. Written messages are convenient for both the sender and the receiver. The sender can prepare the message at a location other than his or her office and can do so during or outside regular work hours. The receiver may read the message at any time or place he or she wishes to do so.

*Be receptive; provide feedback.*

**WORKPLACE CONNECTIONS**

Recognize your personal biases and set them aside when you communicate.

*Written messages are important in business.*

### SELECTING A COMMUNICATION MEDIUM

Although written messages have several advantages, they are not appropriate for every situation. Describe a situation in which you believe face-to-face or telephone communication would be better than written communication. Explain which method is better and why it would be more effective.

Situation:


Explanation:

## CHAPTER SUMMARY

- ◆ Effective communication is important to workers and the organizations that employ them.

- ◆ Communication may be described by its mode, destination, flow, and style.

- ◆ Messages must be ethical and legal.

- ◆ The written communication process involves a sender who encodes a message then transmits it to a receiver who decodes it and gives feedback to the sender.

- ◆ Poor use of words; incorrect or incomplete content; poor organization; wrong channel; grammar, spelling, and punctuation errors; and receiver mistakes are barriers to communication success. Avoiding these problems is crucial to good communication.

- ◆ Written communications play an important role in the workplace because they can be kept, serve as legal contracts, be revised, be sent to many recipients, and are convenient to write or read.

Go to the Grammar and Usage tab; access and read the lesson on Editing, Proofreading, and Spelling. Complete the appropriate *words@work* exercises.

words@work

1. Indicate whether the following items are internal or external messages and whether you would recommend they be prepared in formal or informal style.

| Item | Internal or External | Formal or Informal |
|---|---|---|
| An annual report to stockholders | | |
| A memo telling employees that the cafeteria will be closed for six weeks during remodeling | | |
| An e-mail canceling a meeting | | |
| An e-mail announcing that the company's founder died of a heart attack | | |
| A sympathy message to the company founder's spouse | | |
| A news release announcing plans to expand a corporation's US headquarters | | |
| A letter urging customers to complete a survey | | |
| An e-mail inviting a new employee to lunch | | |

2. Indicate whether each item below is an example of verbal communication, nonverbal communication, or both. Circle the appropriate response. V = verbal, N = nonverbal, B = both

   a. A coffee cup stain on a letter      V    N    B

   b. Forgetting to enclose a brochure with a letter      V    N    B

   c. A "While You Were Out" message to phone a client      V    N    B

   d. A poster outlining a store's return policy      V    N    B

   e. A smudged photocopy of an invoice      V    N    B

   f. A form with boxes too small to fill in      V    N    B

   g. An envelope on which the receiver's name is misspelled      V    N    B

   h. Using a pen to make a correction on a memo      V    N    B

3. Assume that you receive the following e-mail from a group whose purpose is to encourage volunteerism.

> When you travel for business or pleasure, collect the unused toiletries such as shampoo, lotion, and soap from your hotel room and take them to Helping Hand. We'll distribute them to the needy.

Is the action requested above legal? Is it ethical? Present your opinions in an e-mail message to your instructor. If e-mail isn't available, write your paragraph below.

4. Access the Web site at *http://csep.iit.edu/codes/codes.html* or the site at *http://www.depaul.edu/ethics/codes1.html.* Select links for companies or occupations that interest you. Read two of the codes and note the similarities between them. Report those similarities as part of an informational memo to your instructor.

5. The following list contains words used in Chapter 1. For each word, check if it is in your use vocabulary, your recognition vocabulary, or neither. Use a dictionary or thesaurus to learn the meanings of words you don't know.

| WORD | Use Vocabulary | Recognition Vocabulary | Neither |
|------|----------------|------------------------|---------|
| chagrin | | | |
| demographic | | | |
| entity | | | |
| hamper | | | |
| impede | | | |
| jeopardized | | | |
| manifests | | | |
| mode | | | |
| oxymoron | | | |
| prevalent | | | |

*Chapter 1: Understanding the Communication Process*

6. Assume that you hired a local company to clean the furniture in your home or apartment. Six months later, you received the following message. What nonverbal message does the letter send? Record your response beneath the message.

Dear Customer

Thank you for letting us clean you furniture. So that we might continually strive to provide the sort of service you expect, we ask that you compleat the following questioneer.

| | | |
|---|---|---|
| 1. Was the clearner punctial? | Yes | No |
| 2. Was he neat? | Yes | No |
| 3. Was the carpet cleaned to your expections, considering age and ware? | Yes | No |

do you have any suggestions to offer for questions answered "no?

_____

_____

_____

In appreciation for your timely response, here's a cupon for a free sandwich at Freddies on Fourth Street. The cupon can be used between November 20 and 31. A self-addressed envelop is inclosed.

Nonverbal Messages:

7. Rewrite or key in the following message to replace the connotative words and phrases with denotative ones.

We recently surveyed lots of our workers and learned that most would like some exercise equipment in the locker room. We checked around and found that we could buy a few pieces of equipment without spending lots of money. Of course, the locker room will need some remodeling. If you approve this proposal soon, we can have the work done fast.

8. The organizations in the following list have all experienced negative publicity because of perceived unethical practices. As your instructor directs, work with two or three of your classmates to research one of the cases. Your goal is to identify the actions the organization took to remedy the problem and the role communication played in the problem and the solution. You may use electronic resources, print resources, or both. Prepare a brief (1- or 2-page) informal report and be prepared to discuss your findings in class.

Archer-Daniels-Midland Co.          General Dynamics
Columbia/HCA Healthcare Corp.       NYNEX
International Olympic Committee      Sears

9. Consult the classified advertisement section of a local or regional newspaper for employment opportunities in your occupational field. How many advertisements are there and how many list communication skills as a desirable qualification? Are the references general (e.g., ability to communicate) or specific (e.g., write letters, prepare reports, greet clients)? Summarize your findings in a memo to your instructor.

10. Match the terms in the first column with the definitions in the second column by writing the appropriate letter in the blank. Use each letter only once.

_____ barrier                     a. communication blocker

_____ channel                     b. concrete, specific words

_____ connotative                 c. electronic or paper

_____ denotative                  d. highly structured

_____ feedback                    e. messages exchanged by peers

_____ formal style                f. memos

_____ horizontal flow             g. questions or comments

_____ internal communication      h. vague; sense-based words

_____ mode                        i. verbal or nonverbal

_____ use vocabulary              j. words used with confidence

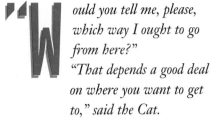

# PLANNING WRITTEN BUSINESS MESSAGES

"Would you tell me, please, which way I ought to go from here?"

"That depends a good deal on where you want to get to," said the Cat.

"I don't much care where—" said Alice.

"Then it doesn't matter which way you go," said the Cat.

At first glance, this quote from *Alice's Adventures in Wonderland* may not seem to have much to do with business writing. A closer look, however, reveals there is a strong, positive relationship between the quote and goal setting—an important element in planning business messages.

## 2 CHAPTER

## PLAN BEFORE YOU WRITE

A **plan** is a set of steps or tasks that must be completed to reach a goal. Little in life gets done without planning, and communication is no exception. Sometimes planning occurs quickly—almost subconsciously, as for a quick e-mail to a friend. At other times, planning is slow and methodical, as for a formal report. The factors that affect the depth to which planning occurs are (1) the complexity of the situation and (2) your familiarity with the task. The more complex or unfamiliar the task, the longer and more structured the planning must be.

During your first few weeks on a new job, you may be nervous. Your surroundings, your coworkers, and the tasks you perform may be unfamiliar to you and, therefore, seem complex. At this stage, you will probably spend a great deal of time planning how to complete the tasks you are assigned. You may ask questions and take notes. If your work includes writing, you will probably prepare an outline and at least one draft before you finish the document.

As time passes, you will become more comfortable in your work environment and more confident about your ability to complete tasks efficiently and effectively. Planning will become more automatic and take less time. When you write, you may not need to create an outline or many drafts. You will still *plan*, but the activity will be more mental than physical.

*Planning is essential for good writing.*

### WORKPLACE CONNECTIONS

Much of the writing you do on the job is routine.

*Follow five steps to plan a written business message.*

**❝ Failing to plan is planning to fail. ❞**

(Source Unknown)

*Set general and specific goals.*

*General goal = why you are writing.*

• *Ask for information*

• *Provide information*

Planning saves time, reduces stress, minimizes communication barriers, and helps writers produce higher quality messages. The process has five steps:

*Step 1:*   Determine your goals.

*Step 2:*   Analyze the situation and receiver.

*Step 3:*   Select the distribution method.

*Step 4:*   Identify content.

*Step 5:*   Gather materials and organize the message.

# STEP 1: DETERMINE YOUR GOALS

How do you measure personal success? You can use *quantitative* measures—GPA, salary, points scored, or pounds lost. You can use *qualitative* measures—contentment, happiness, or security. Whatever specific measure you choose, you determine success by comparing results to preset goals. The same is true in business communication.

Before beginning to write, it is important that you identify general and specific goals. All messages have both, and clarifying them is the first step in the planning process.

## General Goals

Determine the **general goal** by asking "Why am I sending this message?" Frame your response broadly: to inquire, to inform, to persuade, or to build goodwill. These goals reflect the transactive nature of an exchange between sender and receiver(s).

INQUIRE.  To inquire is to ask a question. Your goal is to obtain data or information. The key to writing a successful inquiry is being specific. The following are examples of inquiry messages:

1. A memo to the training coordinator asking whether space is still available in next week's seminar about conducting performance appraisals.

2. A letter to a supplier asking why a quantity discount was not applied to a bill.

3. An e-mail message to the Information Systems department requesting advice about installing a local area network.

INFORM.  Messages that inform provide information. A successful informative message has three characteristics: clarity, completeness, and timeliness. First, the message must be written so the receiver clearly understands its content. Second, the message must contain all the information the receiver needs to act or decide. Third, the message must arrive in time for the receiver to consider and/or act on its contents. The following are examples of messages that inform:

1. A report detailing the costs and benefits of selling the corporate jet.
2. A letter responding to a customer's request for information about treadmills.
3. An e-mail canceling a planning committee meeting.

PERSUADE.  Persuasive writing uses logic and/or emotion to influence a reader to react in a particular way. An effective persuasive message clearly states what to do and why it is important to do so. Persuasive messages stress how the reader will benefit from the proposed action. The following are examples of persuasive messages:

• *Influence*

1. A memo recommending that your department purchase a new printer.
2. A flyer promoting an elementary school carnival.
3. An e-mail encouraging employees to donate to a charity.

BUILD GOODWILL.  All messages should build goodwill between a sender and receiver, but some messages have it as their only goal. These messages are designed to make the reader feel important or special. They bring to the business environment the kindness and courtesy shown in personal or social interactions. The following are examples of goodwill messages:

• *Create or maintain goodwill*

1. A handwritten note added to a sympathy card for your secretary, whose mother died last weekend.
2. A letter congratulating a customer on moving into a new building.
3. A memo thanking a colleague for suggesting a more efficient way to process a claim.

Sometimes messages have more than one general goal. A message designed to convey bad news, for example, informs and persuades. The message *informs* readers of the negative information in a way designed to *persuade* them to accept the news or an alternative solution.

*Messages can have several goals.*

## Specific Goal

The **specific goal** of the message answers the questions "What results do I want?" or "What action do I want the receiver to take?" The following examples show the relationship between general and specific goals:

*Specific goal = what you hope to achieve.*

1. Message:            A letter to clients of your insurance agency.
   General Goal(s):  To inform; to persuade.
   Specific Goal:     To announce a rate increase and retain policyholders.

2. Message:  An e-mail containing inventory data requested by your manager.

   General Goal:  To inform.

   Specific Goal:  To provide information to be used in planning future purchases.

3. Message:  Letter congratulating a client recently elected to the city council.

   General Goal:  To build goodwill.

   Specific Goal:  To commend client for her dedication and willingness to serve.

Recall from Chapter 1 that all messages, regardless of their general or specific goals, must be both legal and ethical.

## CHECKPOINT 2-1

## DETERMINING THE GOALS OF A MESSAGE

**Identify the general and specific goals in the following messages:**

1. An e-mail requesting approval to take vacation March 3–7.

   General Goal(s): _____

   Specific Goal: _____

2. A report describing the status of a remodeling project that is behind schedule.

   General Goal(s): _____

   Specific Goal: _____

3. A letter to a government agency requesting clarification of a regulation.

   General Goal(s): _____

   Specific Goal: _____

4. A business expansion plan that will be submitted as part of a loan application.

   General Goal(s): _____

   Specific Goal: _____

5. A corporation's annual report to shareholders.

   General Goal(s): _____

   Specific Goal: _____

*Chapter 2: Planning Written Business Messages*

# STEP 2: ANALYZE THE SITUATION AND RECEIVER

Both the situation and the receiver must be considered when you plan a writing strategy.

## The Situation

Assess the environment in which you and the receiver operate. Some aspects of the environment are physical, others are political. Time, distance, equipment, sensitivity, and relationships play a role in determining what, when, where, and how to approach communication. Your analysis of the situation, together with your analysis of the receiver, will help you determine how to organize your message, the words you use, and the medium and channel through which you distribute the message.

*Be aware of your physical and political environment.*

## The Receiver

No two people are alike; no two people have the same experiences. These differences make people interesting and make writing a challenge.

Effective communicators choose words their receivers understand. They organize messages to hold a reader's attention. To do these things well, writers must learn all they can about the reader's *knowledge of the subject, interests/motivations,* and *demographic profile*. The writer must determine who will be the primary reader and focus on that person's needs.

WORKPLACE CONNECTIONS

The ability to interact positively with people from diverse backgrounds will make you an asset to your employer.

*Learn all you can about your receiver.*

SUBJECT KNOWLEDGE. Assessing a receiver's knowledge of the subject about which you are communicating helps you choose words and determine content. A reader who is unfamiliar with a subject will not understand its jargon and will need a more detailed explanation than will a reader who is familiar with the subject.

• *Subject Knowledge*

INTERESTS/MOTIVATIONS. Knowing what interests or motivates a receiver—in general *and* with respect to the situation about which you are communicating—helps you write from the receiver's viewpoint. Interests and motivations also influence the organization of the message and the words used within it. Identify subjects, words, ideas, and other factors to which the reader might be sensitive; avoid them or treat them with care.

• *Interests/Motivations*

Many theories of human motivation exist. One of the most notable theories is that introduced by psychologist Abraham Maslow in 1943. Maslow theorized that people are motivated by five levels of need. As basic needs near fulfillment, individuals move to other levels. Maslow's Hierarchy of Needs is shown in Figure 2-1.

*People are motivated by a variety of needs.*

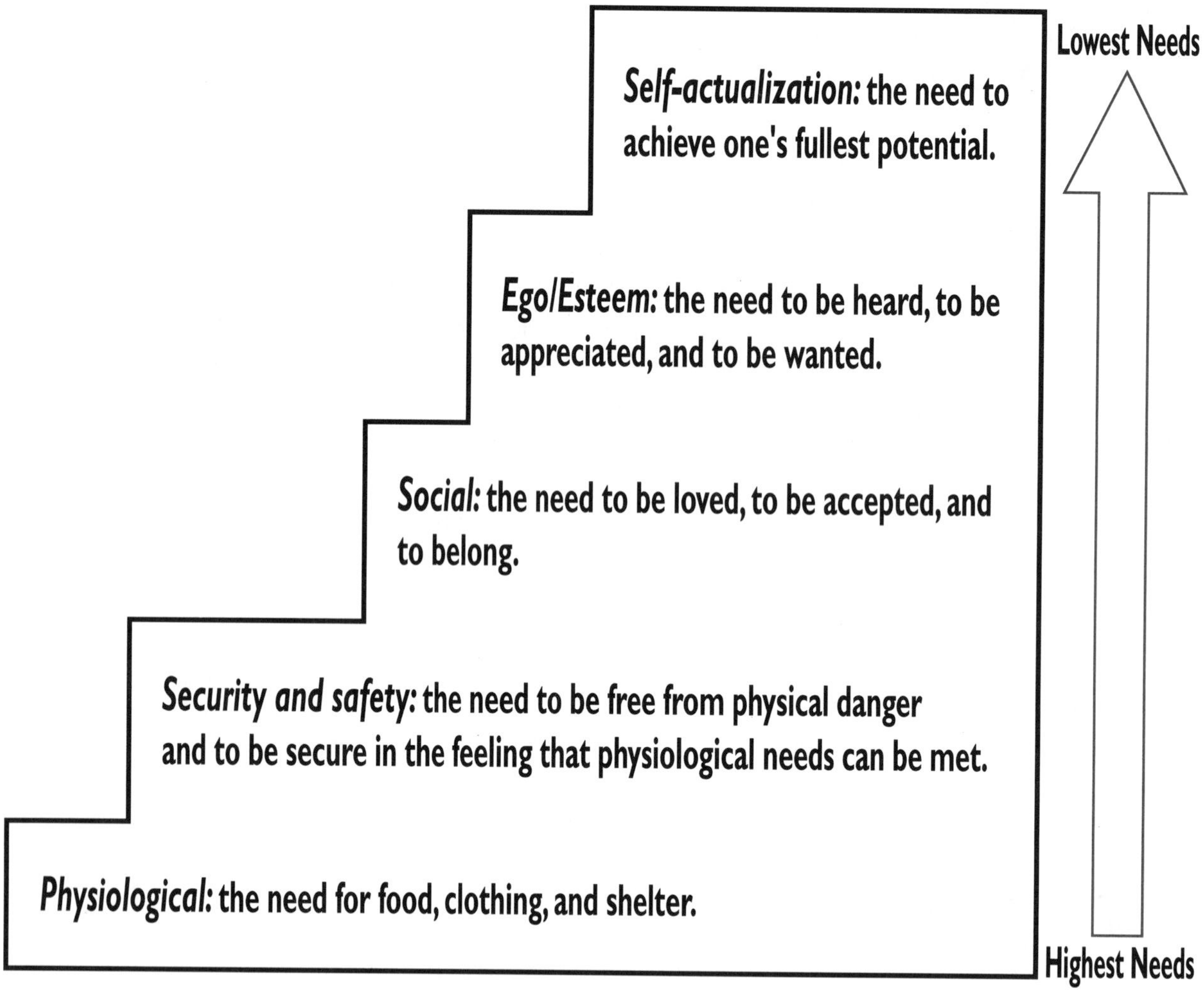

**Self-actualization:** the need to achieve one's fullest potential.

**Ego/Esteem:** the need to be heard, to be appreciated, and to be wanted.

**Social:** the need to be loved, to be accepted, and to belong.

**Security and safety:** the need to be free from physical danger and to be secure in the feeling that physiological needs can be met.

**Physiological:** the need for food, clothing, and shelter.

Lowest Needs

Highest Needs

Figure 2-1
Maslow's Hierarchy of Needs

As you analyze your receiver, determine where the action you seek falls within Maslow's hierarchy. Also determine whether the individual with whom you are communicating will be more influenced by **extrinsic** (external, tangible; e.g., money, promotion) or **intrinsic** (internal, emotional; e.g., pride in work, satisfaction) factors.

DEMOGRAPHIC PROFILE. A demographic profile is a factual picture of an individual or an organization. An individual's demographic profile includes age, race, gender, marital status, number of children, education, religion, occupation, and socioeconomic status. An organization's demographic profile includes size, location, number of employees, and products/services offered. Knowing the reader's demographic profile helps writers send an appropriate message.

Receiver and situation analysis are among the most complex activities associated with business communication. Your ability to analyze receivers will become more astute with experience. Be patient and persistent.

• *Demographics*

*Recognize and respect individual differences.*

*Chapter 2: Planning Written Business Messages*

## RECEIVER ANALYSIS

**Read the following situation and respond to the questions at the end.**

Bill Riley has been a member of the Jupiter Marketing Club for more than 20 years. He has served as program chair, membership director, community service coordinator, secretary, first vice president, and, most recently, treasurer for three consecutive terms. This year, Bill decided to run for president of the club. His opponent is Sally Baker, a three-year member of the club who has chaired the program committee but not held elective office. You've just tallied the votes, and Bill lost the election.

With the information you have available, how do you predict each candidate will react to the election results?

Bill:

Sally:

What additional information would you like to have about Bill and Sally before you notify them of the election results?

Bill:

Sally:

How would your analysis of each receiver and the situation change if Bill had won the election?

# STEP 3: SELECT THE DISTRIBUTION METHOD

Choosing a way to send your message is a two-part process. The sender must select the **medium** through which communication will occur as well as the **channel** through which it is distributed.

## Distribution Medium

Four types of business messages are letters, memos, e-mails, and reports. Letters and memos are often referred to as correspondence. E-mail, though it serves a similar purpose, is typically not included in that classification. Each item will be described briefly in the following sections. Guidelines for preparing letters and memos are included in Appendix A.

*Choose your distribution medium carefully.*

LETTERS. Businesses use letters to communicate with people outside the organization. For example, letters may be sent to shareholders, potential clients, current customers, suppliers, or government agencies. Messages known as **personal business letters** are used when individuals write to organizations. Some organizations use letters to communicate with their employees about important personnel matters.

*Use letters for external messages or formal internal messages.*

Letters are the most formal type of correspondence. They should be printed on good quality bond paper that has been imprinted with the company **letterhead**. A letterhead contains vital information about the organization. Name, address, and phone number have always been the "top three" in letterhead information. Including fax numbers, e-mail addresses, and Internet URLs is becoming commonplace. These items provide information readers need to respond to messages. A logo, a slogan, and/or the names of people who have key roles in the organization also may be displayed on the organization's stationery. In large organizations, upper-level managers and individual departments have their own letterhead. Figure 2-2 contains examples of company and departmental letterhead stationery.

*Letterhead stationery contains information about the sender's organization.*

Organizations can create their own letterhead in their word processor and print it from their own color printers each time it is needed. However, it is more costly and time consuming than having commercially printed letterhead stock on hand.

The format of a business letter should include a date, the complete name and mailing address of the receiver, a greeting, message content, a closing, and a signature line. Wording should be conversational but not casual; abbreviations and contractions should seldom be used. The formal appearance of a letter contributes to a positive organizational image.

*Letters use a structured format.*

MEMOS. When people within the same organization write to one another, they do so through **memos**. The writer and reader may work at adjacent desks or in different countries. Location is irrelevant; the binding factor is their association with the organization. A memo would be used, for example, to tell a worker that his or her vacation has been

*Use memos for internal messages.*

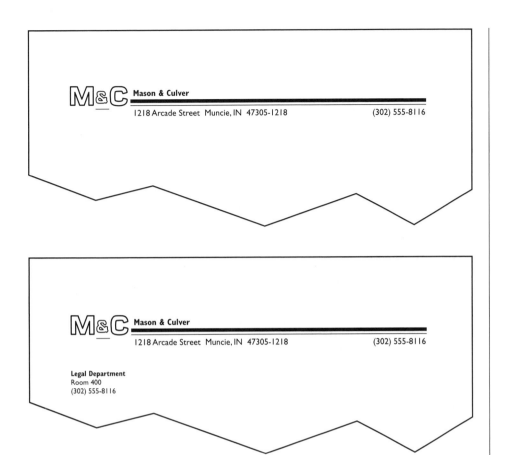

**Figure 2-2**
Samples of Business Letterhead

WORKPLACE
CONNECTIONS

Some companies have developed style manuals that describe the letter, memo, and report formats they want their employees to use.

approved or to announce a contest that all employees are eligible to enter.

Memo formats are less formal than letter formats. Word processing software **templates** offer the writer several formatting options for the "Date," "To," "From," and "Subject" headings found in a traditional memo. Because memos are internal documents, they are often prepared on a lower-quality bond letterhead or on plain paper.

The writing style used for memos also is typically less formal than for letters. More than one receiver's name may be listed in the heading. Courtesy and occupational titles are usually omitted. Abbreviations and contractions are used with greater frequency than in letters. Memos are courteous and respectful, but statements designed to build goodwill are not required. A memo to notify participants about the agenda for a regularly scheduled meeting doesn't need "I'm looking forward to seeing you" at the end.

*Memos are less formal than letters.*

**E-MAIL.** The least formal message is **e-mail (electronic mail)**. The convenience, speed, and ease of e-mail prompt people to use it in place of the telephone or face-to-face meetings. As a result, e-mail can become very casual. Abbreviations (acronyms) and symbols (emoticons) have

*E-mail is convenient, fast, and easy to use.*

become part of the "culture" of e-mail, and correct grammar, spelling, and sentence structure are sometimes set aside. Figure 2-3 shows several common abbreviations and symbols. Tips to help you be a courteous e-mail user are listed in Figure 2-4.

| Acronyms | | Emoticons (turn page clockwise 90° to see "face" | |
|---|---|---|---|
| BTW | by the way | :-I | anger |
| FYI | for your information | :-) | happiness |
| IMO | in my opinion | ;-D | laughter |
| JK | just kidding | :-( | sadness |
| LOL | laughing out loud | :-o | shock; surprise |
| NC | no comment | *,!:-) | ho, ho, ho |
| OTOH | on the other hand | ;-) | wink |

Figure 2-3
Sample E-Mail Acronyms and Emoticons

1. Use a descriptive subject line.
2. All capital letters means you are shouting. Use all capital letters as little as possible.
3. Copy (send) your message only to those who need to receive an original message or a reply.
4. Never send e-mail when you are angry or upset.
5. Check your e-mail at least twice each day.
6. Format messages to fit on small screens as well as large ones so text lines don't break at odd places.
7. Keep messages readable by ensuring they do not exceed one screen page.
8. When replying to a message, avoid including the entire message with your response.
9. Proofread your message for spelling, grammar, content, and organization before sending it; use your e-mail software features to help you.
10. Never say anything in an e-mail that you would not want made public. Messages can be forwarded easily and retrieved from the e-mail system archives even after senders and receivers have deleted them.

Figure 2-4
Tips for Being a Good E-Mail User

The casual nature of e-mail stems from its origin as an internal communication medium. As the Internet has grown, however, use of e-mail has expanded to include communication with external audiences. Today, the following guidelines apply to e-mail:

- When used for internal communication, follow your company's writing style guidelines for memos.
- When used for external communication, follow the conventions for letters.
- When used for personal (nonbusiness) messages, use good judgment, courtesy, and respect.

REPORTS. **Reports** are documents that contain information, data analyses, or recommendations upon which decisions are based. Because of their versatility, reports are a special written communication medium. Their audience can be internal or external; their style, formal or informal. The more components—title page, table of contents, transmittal pages, sections, headings, footnotes, references, index, appendices—the report has, the more formal it is. Although formal reports tend to be longer than informal ones, length is *not* a measure of formality.

Informal reports may be less structured versions of formal reports (fewer components) or they may be formatted as letters or memos. Memo reports are for internal audiences; letters are for external audiences. Sideheadings can be included to guide the reader, just as the headings in this book help you understand the flow, organization, relationship between, and relative importance of items.

# Channel

Your analysis of the situation and the receiver will help you determine the **channel** through which you transmit your message. Channel refers to the way a message is sent. Postal/courier services, fax, and e-mail are examples. Choose a channel that is efficient and effective by considering the number of receivers, speed, cost, access, privacy, retention, and receiver's preference. Appearance is another factor to consider. If it is important that a message look a certain way (in columns, for example), faxing assures that the chosen format will be retained during transmission, while e-mail does not.

The number of channels available to communicators has expanded dramatically in recent years. Letters used to be delivered almost exclusively through the postal service, which offered several delivery classes and services. Courier service was also an option, but cost and distance made it impractical for widespread use.

Today, businesses use a number of delivery services that offer same-day or overnight options at competitive prices. For even faster service, electronic delivery is available by fax or via the Internet. Sometimes a message sender will use several channels. A letter can be sent

*E-mail may be used for internal or external messages.*

**WORKPLACE CONNECTIONS**

Business-related e-mail should be prepared with the same care as other correspondence.

*Reports can be formal or informal.*

*A school term paper is a formal report; a book report is an informal one.*

*Choose a message distribution channel that meets receiver needs.*

*Paper and electronic distribution channels are available.*

electronically to take advantage of speed and in paper form for legal or other reasons.

Whether using a paper or an electronic channel, senders must be sure the receiver's mailing, fax, or e-mail address is correct. A simple character transposition can delay or prevent delivery.

# #@%&!@#

Misdirected e-mail causes problems. Consider the plight of the fellow who decided to e-mail his girlfriend rather than phone her. Because he high-lighted two addresses rather than one in his address file, his message went not only to his girlfriend but also to 1,000 of his coworkers. (*The New York Times*, 10/5/97)

*Ask six questions when identifying content:*
1. *Who?*
2. *What?*
3. *When?*
4. *Where?*
5. *Why?*
6. *How?*

*Brainstorm alone or in a group.*

*Create a cluster diagram.*

# STEP 4: IDENTIFY CONTENT

The content of a message is determined by answering six critical questions: *Who? What? When? Where? Why?* and *How?* A writer should first answer these questions from his or her point of view. Then, he or she should assume the role of message receiver and answer the questions from that person's perspective. Only by looking at a situation from both sides can the writer be sure all essential information will be included in a message.

If the subject of the message is simple or routine, answer the six critical questions by jotting down notes before you compose the letter or memo. When you respond to an e-mail message, use the "reply" function and keep the incoming message on the screen until the response has been drafted. Then you can decide whether to delete the original message or add the reply to it and send the entire document.

For unfamiliar or complex writing tasks, writers often turn to either **brainstorming** or **cluster diagramming**.

## Brainstorming

In **brainstorming**, writers list the items they *might* include in the message. Ideas are listed randomly, without regard to quality, form, order, or priority. One strength of brainstorming is that it can be done alone or with a group. Group brainstorming can be used even when only one person prepares and signs the message.

After the ideas have been recorded, review the list. Add, delete, or combine ideas to reflect the subject, receiver, situation, and goals of the message.

## Cluster Diagramming

Cluster diagramming, like brainstorming, involves listing ideas without prejudging them. However, with **cluster diagramming**, related ideas are grouped as they are written. A writer might begin by listing the six critical questions. Answers are then written near the question to which they relate. As shown in Figure 2-5, main ideas can form the core of the diagram. Once all ideas have been listed, lines are drawn to connect related ideas. New ideas are added; duplicate ideas are deleted. The remaining ideas are evaluated for use in the final document.

*Chapter 2: Planning Written Business Messages*

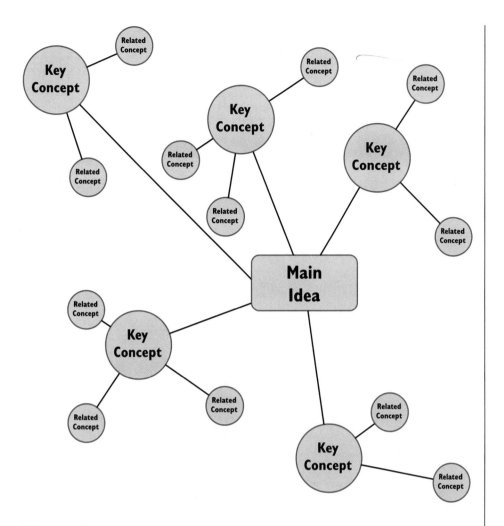

Figure 2-5
Cluster Diagramming

# STEP 5: GATHER MATERIALS AND ORGANIZE THE MESSAGE

After choosing the ideas to be included in a message, the writer gathers and organizes supporting materials.

## Gather Materials

The information to be included in a message can come from a variety of sources, including records kept by the organization. Depending on the data, the writer may need to access and review forms, correspondence, spreadsheets, databases, reports, manuals, or a variety of other in-house materials.

Pamphlets, brochures, books, journals, and the Internet are useful external resources. Writers also may collect new data. Surveys, observations, and interviews are some ways to collect current data.

*Gather necessary material from internal and external sources.*

*Use print and electronic resources.*

# Select an Organizational Approach

The final step in the planning process is organizing the message. The writer chooses a **direct** or an **indirect** pattern (see Figure 2-6).

DIRECT ORGANIZATION.  Using a **direct** pattern means the writer presents the main idea first. Supporting facts or ideas are presented after the main idea. If the writer expects the reader to have a neutral or positive reaction to the message, the direct approach is best. This approach works well for messages designed to inquire, build goodwill, or inform.

INDIRECT ORGANIZATION.   Writing **indirectly** means supporting ideas are presented before the main idea. This technique can be especially effective when writing to persuade or to convey bad news. If the writer expects the reader to have a negative reaction to the message, the indirect approach will have a greater chance of success.

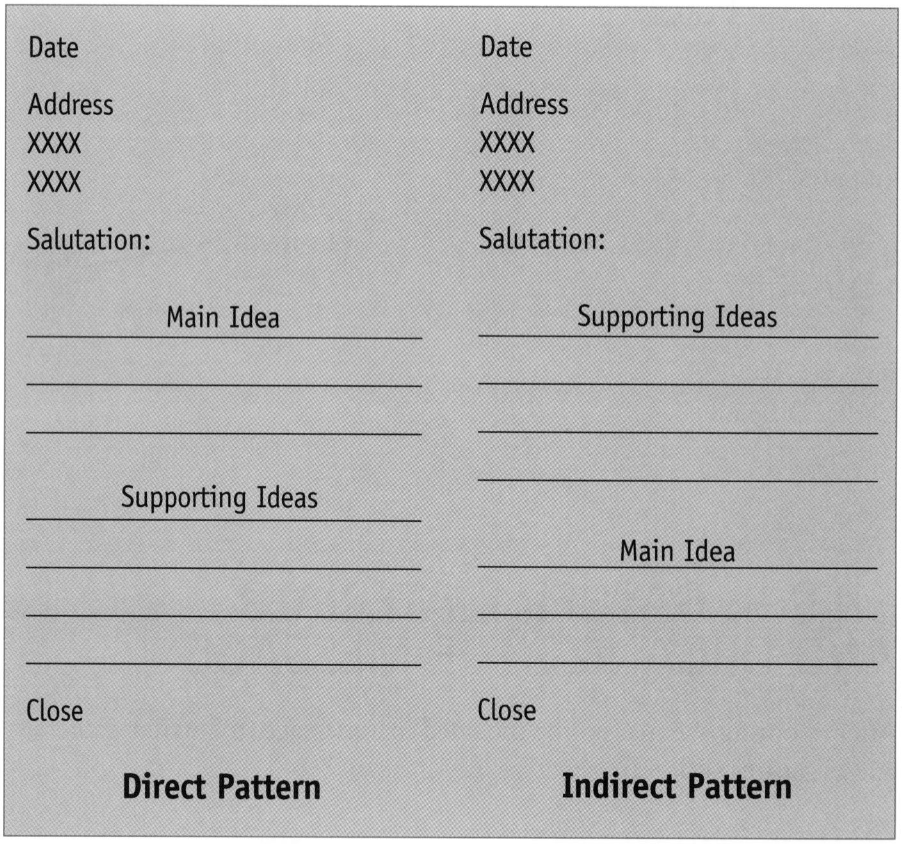

Date

Address
XXXX
XXXX

Salutation:

Main Idea
_____
_____
_____

Supporting Ideas
_____
_____
_____

Close

**Direct Pattern**

Date

Address
XXXX
XXXX

Salutation:

Supporting Ideas
_____
_____
_____

Main Idea
_____
_____
_____

Close

**Indirect Pattern**

Figure 2-6
The Organizational Plans

# APPLY THE PLANNING PROCESS

As office manager for Metropolitan Clinic, you are often called upon to write letters and memos that will be reviewed and signed by the physicians. Today, you've been asked to prepare a message for Dr. Martin Martinez. One of his patients is moving to another state and has asked to have records forwarded to a physician there. After speaking briefly with Dr. Martinez, you identified the following ideas to include in the message:

A. Good luck in new location

B. Records have been sent

C. Patient's son Jordan was first baby Dr. Martinez delivered

D. Appreciation

E. She has a health-conscious family

Answer the following questions based on your analysis of the situation and the receiver:

1. What is your general goal? _____

2. What is your specific goal? _____

3. What medium will you choose? _____

4. What channel will be best? _____

5. What organizational approach will you use? _____

6. How will you arrange the ideas to conform to that approach? (List by topic letter sequence; e.g., A, B, C)

_____

# CHAPTER SUMMARY

♦ Time spent planning is time well spent. Good planning reduces time spent in revising and helps ensure the success of the communication process.

♦ Good writing follows five planning steps:

1. Determine your goals. Always know why you are writing and what you expect to accomplish. Inquire, inform, persuade, and build goodwill are general goals. Each specific goal is linked to a general goal but lists a specific action or result.

2. Analyze both the situation and the receiver. A single receiver may not behave the same way in two different situations.

3. Select the distribution method. Messages may take several forms and be distributed in numerous ways. Choices should be based on the receiver's needs while considering the sender's constraints.

4. Brainstorm content. Writers should list all possible ideas, even if they later decide not to use some.

5. Gather materials and organize the message. Sometimes content will be obvious; other times, content will be based on research. Messages are organized based on how the writer thinks the reader will react to their content. The direct approach is used when the receiver is seen as having a positive or neutral attitude; the indirect approach is used when the receiver is seen as having a negative attitude or must be persuaded.

words@work Go to the Writing Tab; access and read the lesson on Writing in the Workplace. Complete the appropriate *words@work* exercises.

1. Assume that you invited your boss to be the speaker at a meeting of a civic club to which you belong. Although you provided detailed information about the group, the occasion, and the location, your boss's presentation fell short of what you expected based on your assessment of his workplace presentations. Instead of being brief and light-hearted, the presentation was long and technical. In addition, the presentation left much to be desired; eye contact was poor, gestures were distracting, and delivery was monotone. You learned the next day that just before leaving the office, your boss was notified that a major customer had canceled an order. As program planner for the club, you must send your boss a thank you note.

   Analyze the receiver and the situation:

2. Imagine the time when you might own and operate your own business. Use a word processing or graphics program to design a letterhead that could be used by that business.

3. Select one of the following topics—or one of your own, with approval of your instructor. Use Internet or traditional library resources to locate a journal or magazine article that addresses the topic. Summarize the article in an e-mail message to your instructor.

   • office politics

   • gender communication in the workplace

   • intercultural communication

   • e-mail privacy

4. For each of the following situations, indicate whether a letter, memo, personal business letter, or e-mail message would be most appropriate and whether the message should be organized directly or indirectly.

| Situation | Message Type | Approach |
|---|---|---|
| a. Congratulate a friend who was recently elected vice president of a student club at your school. | _____ | _____ |
| b. A customer's order will be delivered on time. | _____ | _____ |
| c. Tell the workers in your office that the alarm system will be tested at 2 PM Wednesday. | _____ | _____ |
| d. Encourage your supervisor to replace the monitor on your computer. | _____ | _____ |
| e. Last month's issue of your favorite magazine has not been delivered to your home yet. | _____ | _____ |
| f. The meeting scheduled for 10 AM today has been canceled. | _____ | _____ |

5. Number the following ideas to show direct organization and then to show indirect organization.

| Direct | Indirect | Paragraph in an application letter |
|---|---|---|
| _____ | _____ | a. worked 16 to 20 hours per week |
| _____ | _____ | b. maintained B- average |
| _____ | _____ | c. attended school full time |
| _____ | _____ | d. organized, self-motivated, successful person |
| _____ | _____ | e. member of Beta Kappa Alpha business society |

| Direct | Indirect | *Memo to all employees* |
|--------|----------|-------------------------|
| _____ | _____ | a. sheets posted by elevator on each floor |
| _____ | _____ | b. brochures about donor qualifications are at reception desk |
| _____ | _____ | c. you could save someone's life |
| _____ | _____ | d. bloodmobile will be at office the week of March 16 |
| _____ | _____ | e. sign up by February 28 |
| _____ | _____ | f. may donate during work hours |

| Direct | Indirect | *E-mail message to people who will interview candidates for a job* |
|--------|----------|-------------------------------------------------------------------|
| _____ | _____ | a. interviews will be scheduled for first two weeks of August |
| _____ | _____ | b. candidate list has been reduced to five |
| _____ | _____ | c. hold the following times/dates for your 30-minute interviews |
| _____ | _____ | d. 47 applications were received for the accounting clerk position |
| _____ | _____ | e. we hope to have a new clerk hired by September 1 |

6. Work with three or four of your classmates to prepare a demographic profile of your business communication class. Submit your profile to your instructor or meet with another team to compare your results.

Consider what subject knowledge the *class* has about the following topics. What interest or motivation might members have to read a message with the goals shown in parentheses?

- federal tax law changes (inform; persuade to use tax service)
- database software (inform of need to buy personal copy)
- life insurance (persuade to buy term insurance)
- stock market (persuade to invest in a mutual fund)

7. Divide your class into two groups. Each group is to decide what content to include in a document titled, "E-mail Use Policy at [name of your school]." One group will use brainstorming and the other will create a cluster diagram.

8. Visit the Web site at *www.albion.com/netiquette/index.html*. Among the things you will find there is a 10-item quiz to measure your "netiquette" ('net etiquette). Take the quiz and e-mail your score to your instructor, with a comment about any questions you may have missed.

9. Write a paragraph describing a situation where communication was strained or failed because the sender did not analyze the receiver. The situation can be one you have observed or one in which you were a participant. The communication may have been oral or written.

10. Collect samples of three business messages. Read the messages to determine the general and specific goal of each. Read the messages to determine whether each was organized by the direct or indirect approach. Report your findings in a brief memo to your instructor.

# DEVELOPING BUSINESS MESSAGES

Once the planning process has been completed, you'll be ready to put your thoughts into words and ready to draft your business message. You'll polish that draft and, after proofreading, have a document ready to be forwarded to your receiver. By applying several principles as you draft, revise, and edit, you'll ensure the success of the communication process.

## APPLYING THE 4Cs OF GOOD BUSINESS WRITING

The primary goal of all communication is receiver understanding. Business writing has the additional goals of being efficient while promoting goodwill. To meet these goals, writers apply principles of good writing known as "The 4Cs"—clarity, completeness, conciseness, and correctness.

### Clarity

**Clarity** is achieved when the receiver understands a message as the sender intended. Word choice, unity, coherence, and structure affect clarity. Each of these factors is explained more fully in the following paragraphs.

WORD CHOICE. Choose short, familiar words your receiver will understand. Use *try* rather than *endeavor*, *guess* rather than *supposition*, and *warning* rather than *admonition*. A print or electronic thesaurus is a valuable tool in choosing clear, simple words.

Clear words are often called "talk" words because they are used in day-to-day speaking. Slang is also part of day-to-day speaking, but it is too casual to be used in business writing. Because slang varies by age, gender, culture, and region, its meaning may not be clear to a larger audience.

> ### LEARNING OBJECTIVES
>
> - Apply the 4Cs of good business writing—clarity, completeness, conciseness, and correctness.
> - Use a positive, unbiased, reader-centered tone.
> - Draft business messages.
> - Overcome writer's block.
> - Use traditional and electronic methods to revise, edit, and proofread messages.

*Clear words are short and familiar to the receiver.*

### WORKPLACE CONNECTIONS

When communicating across cultures, use English that is jargon-free and that avoids buzzwords, clichés, humor, and slang.

*Use jargon and abbreviations carefully.*

*Choose specific words.*

Every occupation has **jargon**, words with special meaning to the people who work in it. Jargon is common words used in uncommon ways. *Noise, bus, culture,* and *virus* have different meanings depending on the profession of those who use them. Use jargon only when you are certain your receiver understands it. If you use jargon, explain each word simply the first time you use it. After the word has been defined, you can use it freely.

Be cautious, too, when using abbreviations and acronyms. An **acronym** is a word formed from the initial letter of major parts of a compound term. FTE (full time equivalent), and CPU (central processing unit) are acronyms. Some acronyms are pronounced as words, such as ESOP (employee stock ownership plan) and LIFO (last in, first out). Abbreviations and acronyms that are meaningful to you may be meaningless and confusing to your receiver.

Concrete words are more understandable than abstract words. **Concrete** words convey one—and only one—meaning. They are specific and vivid. **Abstract** words are vague and imprecise. They may mean different things to different people. *Many* is less specific than *most. Most* could be made more specific by stating a number or percent. *Vehicle* is less specific than *car* or *truck. Car* and *truck* could be made more specific by adding details such as make, model, style, age, and color. Be as specific as necessary to convey the desired meaning to your receiver.

## CHOOSING SIMPLE, CONCRETE WORDS

Assume you are writing to someone with an 8th grade education. Use a print or electronic thesaurus to find three words that can be used in place of each of the following words.

a. capitulate  _____

b. complementary  _____

c. impeccable  _____

d. impetuous  _____

e. pragmatic  _____

Write a concrete word or expression for each of the following abstract words.

a. early  _____

b. many  _____

c. recently  _____

d. small  _____

e. tall  _____

UNITY. Sentences and paragraphs have **unity** when they have one main idea and the other information in the sentence supports that main idea. The first sentence in each of the following sets lacks unity. Clarity is improved in the second sentence of each set.

Today is Monday; London is in England.
Today is Monday; on Thursday we leave for London.

The food is great, and the plant needs direct sunlight.
The food is tasty; the plants help create a home-like atmosphere.

A topic sentence is the most common way to create unity within a paragraph. The topic sentence may be the first or last sentence in the paragraph. In direct construction, the topic sentence opens the paragraph; in indirect construction, the topic sentence ends the paragraph. The approach used within a message may vary from paragraph to paragraph. You may recognize these patterns as being similar to the approaches used to organize messages.

*Each sentence and paragraph should have one main idea.*

*Organize paragraphs by either the direct or the indirect approach.*

COHERENCE. Unified messages are also **coherent**. They flow naturally and the ideas in them relate to each other. Transitional words and phrases and repetition help make messages coherent.

*Transitional words and phrases.* Writers use transitional words and phrases as bridges to join ideas. Additional information, cause/effect, comparison, contrast, sequence, and time are common linkages. Each is illustrated in the following examples:

| Linkage | Transitional Word/Phrase |
|---|---|
| additional information | also, in addition, moreover, too, again |
| cause/effect | because, for this reason, therefore, thus, unless, consequently, as a result |
| comparison | likewise, similarly, in comparison, as |
| contrast | although, even though, but, however, in contrast, nevertheless, on the contrary, still, yet, on the other hand |
| sequence | first, second, etc. |
| | last, finally |
| | 1, 2, 3 |
| | a, b, c |
| time | before, after, then, at the same time, at that time, during, in the meantime, currently, previously, soon, while, now |

**Figure 3-1**

*Repetition.* Repeating words and using pronouns in place of nouns are other ways to achieve coherence. The following sentences show these methods:

The pen and pencil **sets** are packed 12 to a box. Each **set** comes in a case that has the look and feel of leather. (repetition)

The pen and pencil **sets** are packed 12 to a box. **They** are available in gold, silver, or woodgrain casings. (pronouns)

# CHECKPOINT 3-2

## WRITING WITH UNITY

Write a one- or two-paragraph biographical sketch of yourself using at least two of the transitions described in the preceding section.

STRUCTURE. Sentence structure can make a message more interesting and enhance clarity. To create interest, use a mixture of simple, compound, complex, and compound-complex sentences. To enhance clarity, eliminate dangling modifiers, misplaced modifiers, and lack of parallelism.

*Structural variety creates interest.*

*Sentence structure.* English has four sentence structures. An example of each follows:

| | |
|---|---|
| *Simple:* | One main clause (subject and verb)<br>Sue will take the package to Ron. |
| *Compound:* | Two main clauses.<br>Sue will take the package to Ron; he is waiting for it. |
| *Complex:* | One main clause and one or more subordinate (dependent) clauses.<br>Before she sorts the mail, Sue will take the package to Ron. |
| *Compound-Complex:* | Two main clauses and at least one subordinate (dependent) clause.<br>Before she sorts the mail, Sue will take the package to Ron; he is waiting for it. |

*Dangling modifiers.* A modifier "dangles" when it has no subject. Here are two examples:

> While jogging along the path, rain began to fall.
> To get a good job, computer skills are essential.

These sentences are unclear because the subjects cannot logically perform the actions described in the modifiers. Rain cannot jog along a path; computer skills do not apply for jobs. Eliminate a dangling modifier by giving it a subject or changing the main clause so the subject applies to the modifier.

> While **I** was jogging along the path, rain began to fall.
> To get a good job, **business graduates** must have computer skills.

Rain doesn't jog.          Computers don't get jobs.

**Figure 3-2**
Dangling Modifiers Make Meaning Unclear

*Place modifiers near
the words to which they
refer.*

A sentence may not be clear when a modifier is too far from the word(s) to which it relates. Notice how the meaning of each of the following sentences changes by moving the modifier:

> **Only** I have the keys to the building. (one person has keys)
> I **only** have keys to the building. (keys to nothing else)
> I have the **only** keys to the building. (one set of keys)
> I have keys to the **only** building. (one building)

> Please let me know the status of the account on **July 31.** (refers to account status on a particular date)
> **On July 31,** please let me know the status of the account. (specifies when status is to be reported)

*PARALLELISM.* Elements within a series, in a listing, or joined by a conjunction must be treated in the same manner—nouns must be matched with nouns, verbs with verbs, and so on. The following sentences illustrate this concept:

| | |
|---|---|
| *Not Parallel:* | Please respond by phone or sending an e-mail message. |
| *Parallel:* | Please respond by phone or e-mail. |
| | |
| *Not Parallel:* | The speech was lively, interesting, and motivated us. |
| *Parallel:* | The speech was lively, interesting, and motivational. |
| | |
| *Not Parallel:* | The candidate is not only interested in protecting the environment but also in creating jobs. |
| *Parallel:* | The candidate is interested not only in protecting the environment but also in creating jobs. |

# CHECKPOINT 3-3

## CORRECTING FAULTY STRUCTURE

Rewrite the following sentences to correct any structural problems they may contain. If the sentence has no errors, write *correct.*

a. While waiting for the bus, a limousine stopped in front of the hotel.

b. Before locking the door, the alarm was set.

c. As I approached the conference room, I heard laughter and people clapping.

d. The television station is limited in the amount of programming it can offer by hardware and finances.

e. My hobbies are jogging, reading, and working crossword puzzles.

## Completeness

A message is complete when all information necessary for a receiver to understand and act is included. What information is "necessary" depends on the writing situation. If questions have been asked, answer them. If a particular action is desired, specify it. If names, dates, locations, or figures are required for the receiver to take action, include them. Be sure you have asked and answered *who? what? when? where? why?* and *how?*

---

## CHECKPOINT 3-4

## WRITING COMPLETE MESSAGES

You are an order processing clerk for a company that makes personalized ink pens. Today, you received the following letter:

> Please send me 100 pens with the following information printed on them:
>
> Shopper's Helper
> (555)102-9384
>
> The pens should be sent to the address shown in the letterhead. Prompt delivery will be appreciated.
>
> Mark Karl

What information has Mark provided to enable you to process his order?

What additional information do you need to process this order?

What options do you have for getting the information you need?

Which option will promote the most goodwill for your company? Why?

---

*Chapter 3: Developing Business Messages*

# Conciseness

Because business professionals are busy, they prefer messages that express thoughts in the fewest words possible. Well-written business messages are only long enough to present all the necessary information.

*Balance conciseness and clarity.*

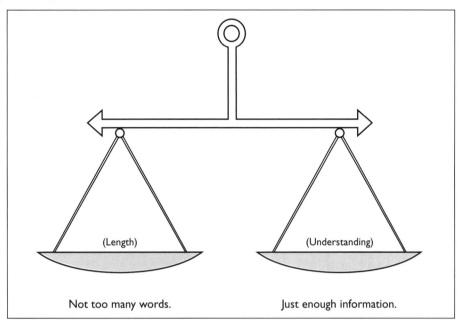

(Length)  (Understanding)

Not too many words.  Just enough information.

**Figure 3-3**
Balance Conciseness and Clarity

The key to writing concise messages, ones that are brief yet effective, is to make every word count. Limit repetition, eliminate excess words, emphasize verbs, and use active voice.

LIMIT REPETITION.  Repeating a word or an idea is one way to emphasize it. Too much repetition, however, is distracting. Two hints for reducing repetition are:

1. Use a shortened form of a noun.
2. Use a pronoun in place of a noun.

> **"** The most valuable of all talents is that of never using two words when one will do. **"**
>
> **Thomas Jefferson**

*Reduce repetition.*

*Original:*  Johan Erickson was office manager for Ador and Smith from June 11, 1995, until February 27, 1998. Johan Erickson was efficient and effective. Johan Erickson worked well with the employees he supervised and scheduled the work of the employees he supervised to assure prompt, correct completion of tasks assigned to the employees.

*Revision:*  Johan Erickson was office manager for Ador and Smith from June 11, 1995, until February 27, 1998. **Johan** was efficient and effective. **He** worked well with the employees he supervised and scheduled **their** work to assure prompt, correct completion of tasks assigned to **them**.

ELIMINATE EXCESS WORDS. A word is excess if it is not needed for correct grammar or clear meaning. Shorten sentences beginning with *It is*, *There is*, or *There are*. Minimize use of *that*. Delete *up*, *down*, *over*, and *under* unless referring to relative position or location. Reduce or eliminate the use of adjectives and adverbs. Eliminate trite and overused expressions such as *henceforth*, *bottom line*, *win-win situation*, and *user friendly*. Rather than use two words with the same meaning, delete one. Whenever possible, use a phrase instead of a clause, a word instead of a phrase.

| *Wordy* | *Concise* |
| --- | --- |
| There are three people who can | Three people can |
| at the time that we were meeting | while we met |
| move up to Canada | move to Canada |
| combine together | combine |
| in the vicinity of | near |
| send back | return |
| at the present time | now |
| due to the fact that | because |
| the meeting on May 10 | the May 10 meeting |

Vary sentence and paragraph length to hold reader interest. A good length for sentences in letters and memos is between 15 and 20 words. Paragraphs of four to six *lines* look inviting and encourage the receiver to keep reading. Sentences in reports may be longer than sentences in letters and memos because reports are often more formal and technical. Sentences in reports should range from 20 to 25 words. Paragraphs should contain 8 to 10 lines.

EMPHASIZE VERBS. Verbs are the most powerful words in the English language. Stressing verbs makes writing concise, clear, and powerful.

| *Weak* | *Powerful* |
| --- | --- |
| find a solution | solve |
| conduct an investigation | investigate |
| make a contribution | contribute |
| be a participant | participate |
| completed the reorganization | reorganized |
| made a selection | selected |

USE ACTIVE VOICE. By using the active voice, writers create messages that are concise, direct, and forceful.

The active voice tells *who* is doing *what*; it stresses the doer of the action. The passive voice tells *what* was done by or to *whom* or *what*. It stresses the receiver of the verb's action and typically includes the words *be*, *am*, *is*, *are*, *was*, *were*, or *been*. Sentences written in the active voice are more clear, direct, and concise.

| | |
|---|---|
| *Active Voice:* | John will conduct a cost-benefit analysis. |
| *Passive Voice:* | The cost-benefit analysis will be conducted by John. |
| | |
| *Active Voice:* | The members elected Carlos Esteban. |
| *Passive Voice:* | Carlos Esteban was elected by the members. |
| | |
| *Active Voice:* | You have not paid your April bill. |
| *Passive Voice:* | Your April bill has not been paid. |

In the third example, the active voice sentence is a bit *too* forceful; it accuses the reader of not paying a bill. When using the active voice produces a negative effect, use the passive voice instead. In the example, using the passive voice places emphasis on the bill, not the reader.

Caution: Do not confuse voice with tense. Active voice may be used with present, past, and future tense verbs.

*Passive voice may be tactful.*

## CHECKPOINT 3-5

## WRITING CONCISE MESSAGES

**Rewrite the following paragraph to make it more concise by limiting repetition, eliminating excess words, using strong verbs, and writing in the active voice.**

Reference manuals are certainly valuable tools and definitely wonderful resources for business professionals who write or prepare business messages as part of the work they do. A reference manual may be thought of by writers as a style manual or a "how to" book for writing. Typically, there is information in these reference manuals about grammar, punctuation, capitalization, abbreviations, word division, use of numbers and symbols, and proofreading. Some of these reference manuals also have special additional sections devoted to topics such as technology, filing, and getting a job.

# Correctness

**Errors can be costly.**

A message is correct when content and mechanics are accurate. Check facts (dates, figures, names), grammar, spelling, and punctuation. Errors can be costly. A misplaced decimal or an incorrect digit in a price or an account balance could cause a company to lose money. Grammar and punctuation errors can affect meaning and create a poor impression of writers and their organizations. Misspelling a name could annoy the receiver and result in a serious loss of goodwill and business. Consider the following examples:

- A manager received an invitation to speak at a conference. The date of the meeting was listed as Monday, May 5. A glance at the calendar told the manager that May 5 was a Tuesday. Which was correct, the day or the date? Additional communication was needed to clarify the request. The message was inefficient, ineffective, and possibly irritating.

- An organization printed catalogs and order forms and distributed them to 10,000 people. Customers were offered a 25% discount on orders of $500 or more. The company intended to offer a 2.5% discount. More than 800 orders were received before the error was discovered. The company had to choose between losing thousands of dollars or losing goodwill and customers. A corrected order form and letter of explanation were printed and mailed. Requests for the 25% discount were honored.

- Pat Petersen wrote to her insurance agent asking about special coverage for her computer. She received a prompt response—addressed to Mr. Pat Peterson. Goodwill was damaged. The message was less than effective. Pat wondered whether she could trust information provided by an agent who doesn't recognize the importance of knowing clients' names.

**Check accuracy twice.**

The accuracy of a message should be checked twice. Content should be checked during revision; mechanics should be checked during editing. Always proofread a document before it is signed or sent.

# WRITING IN A POSITIVE, UNBIASED, READER-FOCUSED TONE

Readers react best to messages written with a positive, unbiased, reader-focused tone.

## Positive Tone

**A positive tone is most effective.**

To write with a positive tone, limit the number of negative words in a message. Avoid *no*, *not*, and *never*. Minimize the use of words with negative prefixes such as *dis-*, *im-*, *in-*, and *un-*. Consider each word you use and the impact it will have on your receiver. The words in the following list are among those to which people may react negatively.

| | | |
|---|---|---|
| allege | fault | irritate |
| bad | flaw | limit |
| claim | hate | loss |
| contrary | ignorant | nonsense |
| disagree | immature | penalty |
| disappoint | inadequate | ridiculous |
| error | inconsiderate | stupid |
| fail | inept | unable |

Writers should also use positive tone when creating sentences. Rather than saying what cannot be done, say what can be done. Rather than saying what is wrong, say what is right. Focus on solutions, not problems. Here are some examples:

*Negative Tone:*     The door on Michigan Street will be locked.
*Positive Tone:*     The door on First Avenue will be open.

*Negative Tone:*     Model 113 has not been made since 1988.
*Positive Tone:*     Model 113 has been replaced by Model 114.

*Negative Tone:*     The sweater is not available in brown.
*Positive Tone:*     The sweater is available in red, blue, and black.

## Unbiased Tone

Business writers should address all people with respect and recognize them for their abilities and talents. Good business messages do not stereotype people based on their gender or physical condition.

**GENDER.** Because both men and women contribute to the success of a business, writers eliminate sexist language from their messages. Here are some ways in which this can be done:

1. Use plural rather than singular nouns and pronouns. Pluralizing the pronoun without pluralizing the noun creates a grammar error (pronoun/antecedent disagreement).

   *Biased:*    A **manager** should be interested in the professional development of **his** workers.
   *Neutral:*    **Managers** should be interested in the professional development of **their** workers.

2. Delete the pronoun.

   *Biased:*    Each candidate presented **his** ideas for cutting taxes.
   *Neutral:*    Each candidate presented ideas for cutting taxes.

**❝ Once you replace negative thoughts with positive ones, you'll start having positive results. ❞**

Willie Nelson

*Respect all people.*

*Use gender-neutral language.*

3. Use an article (a, an, the) in place of the pronoun.

*Biased:*   Every teller should keep **her** work area neat and orderly.
*Neutral:*  Every teller should have a neat, orderly work area.

4. Use both masculine and feminine pronouns.

*Biased:*   A driver should be in control of **his** car.
*Neutral:*  A driver should be in control of **his or her** car.
*Neutral:*  A driver should be in control of **her/his** car.

5. Emphasize the job title.

| *Biased* | *Neutral* |
|---|---|
| chairman | chair, head, leader |
| mailman | mail carrier |
| repairman/serviceman | service representative, technician |
| salesman | sales representative, agent |

## CHECKPOINT 3-6

## WRITING WITHOUT GENDER BIAS

How would you respond to someone who suggests that the first pronoun in a set (*his* in "his or her"; *her* in "her/his") shows gender bias?

How can you avoid the perception of gender bias in long documents that use both masculine and feminine pronouns?

Most biased language stereotypes women, but men also can be affected by sexism. The terms *male nurse* and *male teacher* are just as biased as the terms *female doctor* and *lady executive*. Wording that implies a person is unusual because he or she is in a particular profession should be changed.

Do not apply gender terms to groups of workers. Phrases such as *the girls in the office*, *the boys in the print shop*, and *the guys at work* should be changed. *The staff in the office, the workers in the print shop*, and *the people at work* are not only clear but also fair.

*Unbiased language is fair language.*

PHYSICAL CONDITION. A person's physical condition should be viewed apart from his or her ability to do a job. A person whose vision is other than 20/20 has a vision problem. A person with one leg has a mobility problem. These physical conditions become handicaps only when they limit a person's ability to complete a task or perform an action. Glasses or contact lenses improve a person's vision; an artificial limb, crutches, a cane, or a wheelchair improves a person's mobility.

*Stress a person's ability.*

When writing about someone who has a disability, decide whether it is necessary to mention the person's physical condition. Does describing Roberto Sequira as a *deaf accountant* add meaning to a message? Probably not. If the main idea of the message is the reader's need to use sign language or special communication equipment, say so. When it is necessary to refer to a disability, give the person ownership of the condition. A person who has a cold is not referred to as cold; a person who has a developmental disability should not be referred to as mentally retarded. Here's another example:

*Poor:* A ramp will be installed at the west entry for **people who are confined to wheelchairs.**

*Good:* A ramp will be installed at the west entry to provide access for **people who use wheelchairs.**

# Reader-Focused Tone

As you write, imagine yourself seated in your reader's home or office. Picture yourself opening the message and reading it. Does the message reflect the writer's interest in you or your business? Is the message warm and sincere? If the message focuses on the receiver and stresses how she or he will benefit, it is written in the reader's viewpoint.

*Write from the receiver's point of view.*

*Writer Focus:* I was very pleased to learn about your promotion.
*Reader Focus:* Congratulations on being promoted!

*Writer Focus:* I am glad that you have accepted my invitation to the meeting.
*Reader Focus:* Thank you for agreeing to attend the meeting.

| | |
|---|---|
| *Writer Benefit:* | If I receive your vacation request by May 3, I can complete the schedule on time. |
| *Reader Benefit:* | If vacation requests are submitted by May 3, the schedule can be posted by May 15. |

Using the personal pronouns *you* or *your* won't guarantee that a message will stress the reader's point of view. In most cases, changing from the active voice to the passive voice is all that is needed.

| | |
|---|---|
| *Writer Focus:* | I did not receive your payment until after it was due. |
| *Reader Focus but Negative Tone:* | You didn't make your payment until after it was due. |
| *Neutral Tone:* | The payment to your account was received three days after it was due. |

# DRAFTING BUSINESS MESSAGES

The work you did during the planning stage of the writing process will help you draft your message. The outline or list of ideas you created and the organizational plan you selected will be your guide as you convert your thoughts to words, sentences, and paragraphs.

Your goal during this stage of the writing process is to get *something* on paper. Focus on content and logic. Don't worry about grammar, spelling, punctuation, format, or other mechanical factors. Worrying about the mechanical aspects of a draft adds unnecessary pressure and detracts from the primary objective. Once your thoughts have been converted to words, they can be shaped and refined through revision and editing.

*A draft is a work in progress.*

## Writer's Block

Despite thorough planning, some people have difficulty starting to write. Rather than face a blank sheet of paper or a blank computer screen, some writers stall. They look for other things to do. They wait for inspiration. They want the words to flow in final form. They have **writer's block.**

Luckily, writer's block is temporary and can usually be overcome easily. The following techniques can subdue writer's block:

*Writer's block can be overcome.*

* **Commit to the task.** If writing is an integral part of your job, establish a routine. Find a time when you have no commitments and when you know you will be effective. If you are most productive in the morning, make writing one of the first things you do after you arrive at work. Make writing part of your daily routine; let others know you are not to be disturbed during this activity.

- **Clear your mind.** If your head is full of nagging problems or you feel tense or nervous, you won't perform at your peak. Solve problems or set them aside. Take a 5- or 10-minute break, perhaps a short walk; a change of scenery can help to clear your head.

- **Get organized.** Be sure your work area is clean, comfortable, and functional. You will need easy access to files, research notes, a thesaurus, a dictionary, and a reference manual.

- **Plan first.** Even hastily written notes or a mental outline can help focus your thoughts.

- **Set short-term goals.** You can't finish something you haven't started. Set achievable goals and follow through. Your goal can be as simple as writing for five minutes without stopping (free write) or generating two paragraphs before lunch or a scheduled appointment.

- **Be patient.** If you are having trouble opening a message, write another section first. The opening will be easier when you return to it.

- **Remember, it's a *draft*.** The beauty of the writing process is that you can review and change what you've written before it is sent.

Once your message has been developed, let some time pass before you look at it again. The time needn't be long—just enough to give you a fresh perspective. If you are creating an e-mail message, you might leave it long enough to read one or two pieces of incoming e-mail. When you resume writing, you'll have a better perspective and can make changes.

# USING TRADITIONAL AND ELECTRONIC METHODS TO REVISE, EDIT, AND PROOFREAD BUSINESS MESSAGES

Revising and editing are separate processes with separate goals. **Revising** focuses on content; **editing** addresses mechanics. Both functions can be accomplished at the computer keyboard, but printing the document and making notations on the paper copy helps. This technique allows the writer to see the final product with a reader's eye. The symbols presented in Appendix B are often used to show changes.

## Revising

When writers revise messages, they verify content, delete or add material, move text to achieve better flow, strengthen word choice, smooth transitions, and improve tone. Revising may be done alone or with someone else. Reading a message aloud can help, too.

> **❝ Writing and rewriting are a constant search for what one is saying. ❞**
>
> John Updike

*Let time pass between drafting and revising a message.*

*Revising and editing are related, yet different.*

> **❝ In baseball you only get three swings and you're out. In rewriting, you get almost as many swings as you want. ❞**
>
> Neil Simon

**GET A SECOND OPINION.** When messages are long, have complex content, or deal with sensitive topics, it is wise to consult one or more colleagues as you revise. Explain the situation, and ask your coworker to read your draft. Get specific suggestions about how to strengthen content and style.

**READ ALOUD.** Reading your message aloud adds another dimension to the revising process. Hearing your message will heighten your awareness of gaps or weaknesses in logic or to rough transitions between topics or ideas. You'll also get a better sense of whether you've used conversational language and achieved an appropriate, business-like tone.

*Some errors can be heard more easily than seen.*

WORKPLACE
CONNECTIONS

Occasionally asking for help is a sign of strength, not weakness. It demonstrates a commitment to the organization and to the receiver.

*Careless proofreading undermines a writer's credibility.*

## Editing

Business writers revise messages to refine content; they proofread and edit to be sure their messages are mechanically accurate—that spelling, grammar, punctuation, and format are correct. Errors in these areas may inhibit understanding, have an adverse effect on image, or both. Mechanics and format complement content and deserve serious attention.

## Proofreading

Proofreading requires concentration. Because writers have created and revised message content, they tend to see what they think the message says, not what is really there. Fortunately, a number of traditional methods and electronic tools provide assistance. Traditional proofreading methods involve reading, either alone or with a partner. Electronic means involve using the grammar and spell check features of word processing software. Figure 3-4 lists several tips to follow when proofreading.

*Recognize the weaknesses of electronic proofreading tools.*

## Revising Electronically

Writers who use word processing software should remember that spell checkers and grammar checkers are tools, but only tools. Because they do not locate all types of errors or automatically make changes, these tools merely supplement good proofreading. A spell checker, for example, would not identify a keyboarding (form/from) or word choice (principle/principal) error. Appendix D, which contains a list of frequently confused words, will be a useful resource in making word choice decisions.

## Proofreading Tips

◆ Read the document several times, each time with a different goal.

◆ Read the text from bottom to top so that you won't be influenced by context.

◆ Tilt the paper, but not your head, to force concentration.

◆ When using a computer, scroll through the text line by line. The border of the monitor will act as a visual barrier and force concentration.

◆ Watch for punctuation that comes in pairs (like parentheses); be sure both parts of the set are there.

◆ Start at the top of the message; avoid the urge to read only text that is displayed as a paragraph.

◆ Read all text that is displayed for emphasis; avoid the tendency to believe that such text can't contain errors.

◆ Proofread after every revision and editorial change. Be aware of the following errors associated with word processed text:
  • duplication resulting from use of the cut/paste function
  • numeric or alphabetic sequence errors
  • editorial fragments—trying various word combinations and forgetting to delete unwanted text
  • missing transitions due to cut/paste alterations

Figure 3-4
Proofreading Tips

WORKPLACE CONNECTIONS

Make a list of the writing errors you tend to make most often. Post the list near your computer as a reminder to watch for and correct those errors.

**❝ If you have made mistakes . . . there is always another chance for you . . . ❞**

Mary Pickford

# CHAPTER SUMMARY

- ♦ Business writing is clear, complete, concise, and correct.

- ♦ Clarity involves word choice, unity, coherence, and structure.

- ♦ Choose words your receiver will understand.

- ♦ Write sentences and paragraphs that have one main idea.

- ♦ Add interest to your writing by using a variety of sentence structures; create unity by using transitional words and phrases.

- ♦ Be sure your messages include all information the reader needs.

- ♦ Preserve clarity while striving for brevity. Limit repetition, eliminate excess words, emphasize verbs, and use active voice.

- ♦ What you say and how you say it are both important. Be sure the content and mechanics of your message are accurate.

- ♦ Readers will react favorably to writing that has a positive, unbiased, reader-centered tone.

- ♦ Overcome writer's block by being committed to writing, clearing your mind, organizing your work area, planning, setting short-term goals, and being patient.

- ♦ View revising and editing as circular processes; repeat them as many times as necessary to produce well-written messages.

- ♦ Drafting, revising, editing, and proofreading messages take time, patience, and a critical eye.

- ♦ Use collaboration when revising and proofreading long, complex, or sensitive messages.

- ♦ Electronic tools supplement traditional proofreading methods.

words@work Go to the Writing Tab; access and read the lesson on Business Letters. Complete the appropriate *words@work* exercises.

# CHAPTER 3 APPLICATIONS

1. Find simpler words for each of the following complicated words. Use a dictionary or thesaurus as needed.

   a. ambience _____

   b. corroborate _____

   c. exemplary _____

   d. exposition _____

   e. gamut _____

   f. matriculate _____

   g. queue _____

   h. relinquish _____

   i. succumb _____

   j. vivacious _____

2. Find a specific way to describe each vague term in the following list.

   a. hot weather _____

   b. work late _____

   c. office furniture _____

   d. computer _____

   e. keys fast _____

   f. software _____

   g. low cost _____

   h. reliable _____

   i. good salary _____

   j. holiday _____

3. For each of the following sentences, circle Y if the sentence has unity and N if it does not.

a. Y    N    The patient is recovering; the car lights are still on.

b. Y    N    After we left the theater, please put the cards in alphabetical order.

c. Y    N    Although it was only 6 AM in Phoenix, Bill phoned Karl to get his opinion about the report.

d. Y    N    While Martin was on vacation, Julia modified the data base; Angie is ill today.

e. Y    N    Three windows were broken during the storm; an insurance claim has been filed.

f. Y    N    The cafe is popular among tourists, so be sure to make reservations.

g. Y    N    The tire is flat; your VCR will be ready Friday.

h. Y    N    To take advantage of the discount, submit the enclosed coupon with your order.

i. Y    N    The temperature was so high this morning that I was able to walk barefoot in the park.

j. Y    N    As you requested, the proposal will include a budget.

4. Form complete sentences by using transitional words or phrases to link the ideas in each of the following clauses. The type of transition to use is shown in parentheses.

a. (cause/effect)          it was cold outside          Joan wore a wool coat

_____

b. (time)          drive north 3 miles          turn right on Oak

_____

c. (comparison)          the old copier is large and slow          the new one is small and fast

_____

d. (sequence)          prepare a resume          write an application letter

_____

e. (added information)          the monitor is large          the resolution is high

_____

f. (contrast)          I appreciate your thoughtfulness          I must refuse the invitation

_____

*Chapter 3: Developing Business Messages*

5. Rewrite the following items to make them brief.

a. There are four people who can do the job well.

b. The office will be closed for remodeling for several days during the month of April.

c. Because of the fact that Sabra is not available to represent us, the case will be handled by Robert.

d. There were only 50 people in the room when the meeting came to a close.

e. We would like you to sign the form and send it back to us in the envelope that is enclosed with this letter.

f. At the present time we are conducting a survey to determine employee preferences.

g. Adel has developed a low-cost, inexpensive substitute to be used in place of our current method of processing claim forms.

h. Michelle drew a perfectly round circle without using a compass or a pattern.

i. The Jewel Company and Simplex, Inc. are merging their offices and building a modern, up-to-date facility over by the Northberg Mall.

j. It was Madeleine who made the suggestion that we refinance the loan.

6. Send an e-mail to your instructor explaining the difference between text that is short and to the point and text that is curt and bossy.

7. Rewrite the following sentences to eliminate dangling or misplaced modifiers and to correct problems with parallelism.

a. If I had more money, time, or the energy to accomplish tasks, I would lead a simpler life.

b. While traveling in Oregon, the car overheated.

c. Speaking from a worker's perspective, the keyboard should be lower.

d. The soap can be used to remove stains or for doing laundry.

e. She heard the mayor and thousands of other citizens give a report on the growth of the city.

f. You will find more products, faster checkout lines, and you will pay less.

g. Under your dedication and energetic leadership, membership has grown by 15 percent.

h. After checking with your references, the Circle T Cafe has a reputation for paying its bills on time.

i. The report you wrote to the Board of Directors will be presented next Monday.

j. The warranty only applies to the original buyer.

8. Rewrite each of the following sentences to emphasize its verb.

   a. It is Kenneth's intention to resign at the end of the month.

   b. You have our appreciation for your work as a volunteer.

   c. Please issue a replacement for the lost merchandise.

   d. Raul and Samantha had a discussion about office relocation.

   e. Steven said he would make his decision by the end of the day.

9. Change the following sentences from passive voice to active voice.

   a. The orchestra was conducted by Harriet Veldman.

   b. The machine has been repaired.

   c. Dinner will be served at 7 P.M.

   d. The impression he created was positive.

   e. The costume was designed by Margo Jago and sewn by Jack Perkins.

10. Change the following sentences from active voice to passive voice.

a. John Hazard wrote *The Munchkin Mystery*.

b. Sue took minutes at the May meeting.

c. The clerk wrapped the package.

d. Julia, Katya, and William decorated the lobby.

e. The investment club donated $500 to the scholarship fund.

11. Make the following sentences more positive.

a. The wallpaper cannot be hung until the ceiling is painted.

b. Opal will not return from vacation until next Monday.

c. Your order cannot be processed until we receive your deposit.

d. People under age 18 are not eligible to enter the contest.

e. If you do not pay your membership dues, you will not receive the newsletter.

12. Rewrite the following sentences to reflect the reader's point of view or to create a neutral tone.

a. I would like to thank you for subscribing to *Today's Jeweler*.

b. You didn't state the color or size on your order.

c. I appreciate your taking the time to interview me for the assistant manager position.

d. We always like to have you send us comments and suggestions.

e. I want to tell you how much I liked your presentation about the importance of diet and exercise.

13. Rewrite the following sentences to make them gender neutral.

a. Each candidate should submit his resume and a letter of application.

b. Please have your salesman visit us early in March.

c. Joan Manderfeld, a female dentist from Topeka, was selected to be chairman of the fundraiser.

d. A jogger should be sure his shoes provide support and comfort.

e. The councilmen will vote on the issue next Monday.

14. Rewrite the following sentences to focus on people rather than their disabilities.

a. Although he is retarded, George is able to pull customer files with 95 percent accuracy.

b. The Freeport Flyers is a basketball team for people in wheelchairs.

c. Al, the epileptic groundskeeper, plans to open a nursery next spring.

d. The Most Valuable Player award was presented to Fran, a diabetic.

e. The public relations department recently hired a deaf artist.

15. In each of the following items, delete the word that is used incorrectly. Use Appendix D as a resource.

a. We may not need the projector, but pack it any way/anyway.

b. Nan and Jerry will come/go to our home for dinner next Wednesday.

c. The Board of Directors passed/past the resolution at its October meeting.

d. Personal/Personnel problems should be forgotten when the work day begins.

e. Doug and Margo Wilson have invited us to their/there/they're home for a picnic.

f. How will the program affect/effect unionized workers?

g. Bring/Take this package to the mail room.

h. Catalogs will be sent to every one/everyone on the preferred customer list.

i. Assure/Ensure/Insure Mr. Tomiano that repairs will be made promptly.

j. Fewer/Less people attended the meeting this year than attended last year.

16. Use editing symbols [Appendix B] to note where changes are needed in the following document.

November, 31, 20—

Ms. Suzanne Plotz
1234 Abernathy Road
Martinsville, VA 24112-6781

Dear Mrs. Plotz:

After receiving you're letter, we conducted an investigation of your credit transactions for last month. Here is what we found:

| October 3 | Men's Clothing | $119.40 |
|---|---|---|
| October 9 | Cards | 5.12 |
| October 18 | Women's Sportswear | 78.33 |
| | Shoes | 56.90 |
| | Men's Clothing (return) | −29.83 |
| October 23 | Housewears | 18.76 |
| October 29 | Boys' Clothing | 46.42 |
| November 6 | Linens | 27.86 |

According to our records, your purchases during the month of October totaled $295.10. The 15 percent applied to your account due to the fact that you are a you are a new credit card customer reduces the amont you owe to $259.69.

Ms. Plitz, please compare your charge slips with the purchases listed in this letter. If your records show the exact same thing, please submit payment before December 15. Otherwise, phone (123) 555-7275 too schedule an appointment with one of our customer service representatives.

Yours truly,

17. Exchange messages (exercise 16) with another student in your class. Follow the notations and create a final version of the message. Make only the changes noted on the other students' paper. When your paper is returned, proofread it. If it is error-free, sign it; otherwise, mark the editing changes and return it to your teammate. Repeat this process until the message is correct and ready to send.

18. Key the following document as a personal business letter; make all changes noted by editing symbols. The sender is Ailane P. Magnuson, 323 Zircon Way, Macon, Georgia 31206-5833. The receiver is Mr. Isaac Jarow, Vice President for Operations, RPB Corporation, Suite 34A, 905 River Bend Trail, Macon, Georgia 31201-0092.

Dear isaac:

Thank you so much for speaking with me last Friday about the marketing position  the job
you have avail able at RPB Corporation; it sounds fascinating. I especially like the

fact that I would have an opportunity to use the sales training I received while

enrolled as a student at Kragre Business School. As I mentioned during the inter-

view, classes at Kragre end on Friday, June 15, and I would be available to begin

working the following week. I'm looking forward to hearing from you. If I can pro-

vide you with additional information about my qualifications or experience, I will

gladly do so.

Yours truly,

# WRITING POSITIVE AND NEUTRAL NEWS MESSAGES

The United States Postal Service processes more than 600 million pieces of mail each day. More than 50 million U.S. workers have access to e-mail. Americans fax about 70 million pages each year. Not all these messages are business communications, but the numbers are impressive— and data on memos haven't been included! Faced with this level of competition, your messages must attract and hold your reader's attention to get the results you want. In this chapter, we'll explore how the direct approach is used to produce successful positive and neutral news messages.

# 4 CHAPTER

## THE DIRECT APPROACH

The **direct approach** is used for messages the reader will view as neutral or favorable. The following types of messages use the direct approach:

- requests
- replies
- informational messages

A message organized by the direct approach begins with the main idea, the purpose of the message. Putting the main idea first attracts attention and makes receivers want to read more. The supporting details follow in the next paragraph(s). After the necessary details are provided, the writer ends the message positively and courteously.

A good example of the direct approach is a traditional paper memo that announces the agenda for a meeting. The opening states the group's name and the time, day, date, and location of the meeting. Details about the items to be discussed, the order in which they will be handled, and who will be responsible for each would be considered supporting information. If the readers attend this meeting regularly, a courtesy phrase such as *I'll look forward to seeing you at the meeting* is unnecessary. The content of the message will be received neutrally as a part of the reader's regular work. If the message were sent to a guest at the meeting, a forward-looking welcome would be fine.

## LEARNING OBJECTIVES

- Explain the direct organizational approach to writing messages.
- Compose effective requests for information or action.
- Write effective replies.
- Convey unsolicited informational messages clearly and completely.

*Use the direct approach to write messages to which your reader will react positively.*

*Put the main idea before the supporting details.*

*Include all relevant details.*

The direct approach uses location and mechanics to create emphasis.

## Location

*Use location to emphasize important points.*

Location is based on the premise that the first and last positions in a paragraph or message are emphatic. The white space before the first sentence and after the last sentence form a visual break between thoughts. This break gives the text emphasis.

## Mechanics

*Print size, font, and display features also draw a reader's eye.*

Type size, font, boldface, centering, and underscoring can be used to create emphasis. A vertical list with each item introduced by a number, letter, or bullet (symbol) also gives emphasis. The reader's eye is drawn to the items because they stand out. The points in such a listing are referred to as bullet points because they are a target for the reader's eye.

## CHECKPOINT 4-1

### THE BENEFIT OF VERTICAL LISTS

**Use a vertical list as you respond to the following questions:**

In what ways does a vertical list help readers?

In what ways does a vertical list help writers?

# WRITING REQUESTS

The timely exchange of accurate information is essential in every organization, and request messages are the basis of these exchanges. Requests are received from and directed to customers, workers, or other organizations. The specific purpose of your requests can be to (1) ask for information or action, (2) place an order, or (3) make a claim.

Information/action requests and claims may be either direct or persuasive. Your analysis of the receiver's reaction will determine which strategy to use. When you think the reader will view the message positively or neutrally, use the direct approach. If you anticipate that the reader will need to be convinced to respond favorably, use the indirect approach. The direct approach is covered in this chapter; persuasion is covered in Chapter 6.

## Asking for Information or Action

Many of the messages you write on the job will be requests. You could send a memo or an e-mail to someone in another department asking for sales figures. You might write to a supplier asking for information about a product. You might inquire about a form or check that hasn't been received from a client. In your personal life, you might write to your insurance company about coverage for your computer equipment or ask a former teacher to give you a reference for a job. All these requests will have three parts: an opening, a middle, and a close.

THE OPENING OF THE MESSAGE. The opening is a clear statement of your request or a brief lead-in to it. For example, if you saw an ad offering a prospectus for a stock you might want to invest in, your opening might be: *Please send me the investment prospectus for. . . .* In a message containing several specific questions, a good opening would be: *Will you please provide the following information about. . . .* This courteous request would introduce a numbered or bulleted list of questions. Figure 4-1 shows a personal business message that uses a bulleted list.

THE MIDDLE OF THE MESSAGE. The middle clarifies the request or explains why you are making it. Show how the reader will benefit from providing the information or taking the action you request. If you use a list, be sure the questions are clear, specific, and written in parallel form. Make a conscious choice between asking close-ended questions that will generate a yes/no response and open-ended questions that will draw out a longer response. Asking *What service contract length options are available?* will produce more information than asking *Is the service contract length variable?* Beware of close-ended questions that will elicit a confusing response. *Is your service contract fixed or variable?* will get a *yes* answer but no information.

March 2, 20—


Tourism Director
Chamber of Commerce
987 Babcock Trail
Bangor, ME 04402-1174

**Request for Information**

Please provide the following items or information about Bangor and the
surrounding area:

- Local map.

- List of hotels/motels with indoor and outdoor swimming pools.

- List of recreational facilities such as hiking trails, biking trails, and golf
  courses.

- List of special events occurring between June 23 and
  July 6.

- List of specialty shops featuring artwork and antiques.

A reply by April 1 will allow us to finalize our vacation plans early this
spring. My family and I are looking forward to an entertaining, relaxing
visit to Maine.


Blake Amroke
5768 East 7th Avenue
Monroe, LA 71201-3371

Figure 4-1
Personal Business Letter with Bulleted Listing

*Provide all the infor-
mation the reader will
need to respond to the
request.*

THE CLOSE OF THE MESSAGE. The close provides details the reader
needs to comply with the request. Is there a deadline by which you need
a response? State it. Should the response be directed to someone other
than the writer? Give the name and a complete mailing address or
phone/e-mail/fax number. Express appreciation without using trite,
overused, or outdated expressions such as *Thanking you in advance* or *If
you have questions, please let me know.*

Analyze your receiver and the situation as you plan your message. These factors, together with your specific purpose, will help determine the length of your message. Remember that the opening, middle, and close are parts of a message and can be developed as separate paragraphs or combined into one. The following internal e-mail message combines the opening, middle, and close in one brief paragraph.

> What's our current inventory of MS-322s? I need the figure by 1 PM for a report that must go out by 3 PM today. Thanks!

The message combines all the elements of good writing; it is clear, complete, concise, and courteous.

Messages written by individuals to organizations can be succinct, too, as shown in the following example:

> Please remove information about me from all national direct mail and telemarketing lists maintained by your organization or its members.

Beginning the message with *please* makes the action a courteous request to be handled in a timely manner. The reader doesn't need to know why the writer wants to be removed from the list.

It would be unusual to have an external message that was as brief as either of the previous examples. An organization wouldn't want to risk creating such a stark, impersonal image.

## Placing an Order

Most product or service orders are submitted on a seller's paper or online form. In some cases, the form is filled out by the seller's representative during an on-site visit or a telephone call. If a blank form or the telephone number isn't available, send a letter. Make sure the letter contains all the information found on an order form:

- item number
- quantity
- description
- size
- total cost
- delivery destination

- color
- unit cost
- tax
- shipping charges
- payment method
- contact information

Figure 4-2 illustrates a complete order letter.

The opening to the order letter makes it clear that the writer is placing an order, not merely requesting information. The message gets right to the point and ends the same way. Appreciation is integrated into a sentence rather than being added as a separate statement.

**The Treasure Chest**

Towne Plaza • 809 Milford Road
Cheyenne, WY 82001-4568

February 11, 20—


Paxton Products, Inc.
Box 3840-J
Mount Vernon, OR 97865-3840

**MERCHANDISE ORDER**

Please ship the following music boxes and bill both product and shipping costs to account 354901-6.

| ITEM NO. | QTY. | DESCRIPTION | UNIT PRICE | TOTAL PRICE |
|---|---|---|---|---|
| 245-RA | 7 | Rabbit/Here Comes Peter Cottontail | $7.49 | $52.43 |
| 245-CL | 3 | Sad Clown/Send in The Clowns | $8.35 | 25.05 |
| 245-RO | 2 | Rosebud/Anniversary Waltz | $8.35 | 16.70 |

All items are from your spring catalog, which promises delivery within three weeks for orders placed by February 15.


JANICE GRUDER
MANAGER

**Figure 4-2**
Order Letter

> ✢ Statistics show that fewer than half the people who have a valid complaint actually convey their disappointment or concerns to the company involved. When you are disappointed with a product or service, give the company a chance to correct the problem.

## Making a Claim

Despite the good intentions and best efforts of everyone involved in business transactions, things occasionally go wrong. Goods are damaged during shipment, too few or wrong items are delivered, products don't work, or service doesn't meet expectations. Research shows that happy customers tell three friends, unhappy customers tell nine friends. Businesses recognize this fact and the importance of remedying these situations before customers are lost or the organization's image is damaged. Organizations view reasonable, timely claims as positive messages, and writers should use the direct approach when preparing them.

*Claims are good news.*

The opening to a claim is designed to capture the reader's attention and give an overview of the situation. The following sentence illustrates an effective opening statement:

> Three of the chairs in the shipment delivered June 10 arrived with torn cushions.

When the remedy to the problem is obvious, as with replacement or reimbursement, the desired action can be built into the opening. For example:

> Please ship ten 24V CraftMate marine batteries to replace ten damaged 12V batteries delivered as part of the shipment received March 12.

*Be clear from the start of a message that you are making a claim.*

## CHECKPOINT 4-2

## CONTROLLING ANGER, PART 1

Jordan Golden is angry and thinks he has a right to be. The CD player he ordered from a mail order catalog arrived today, in time to be given to his sister on her 13th birthday, but not in gift condition. The digital display cover was cracked, the case was scratched, and the headset cord was frayed. Jordan has drafted what he thinks is an effective claim letter. You disagree and offer to help him revise the message. After reading what Jordan has prepared, write an appropriate opening for his claim.

> Are you people in the business of selling used merchandise? It certainly seems that you are! I sent you $59.95 of my hard-earned money for what I thought would be a nice gift for my sister. Boy, was I wrong! I'll never do business with you people again. I want my money, an apology, a new CD player, and five free CDs. The sooner the better. Hattie's birthday is next week.

In the middle of a message, explain and document the claim. Tell the *who, what, when, where,* and *why* of the problem and *how* it was detected.

Stay calm and be objective. Your reader didn't cause the problem or observe what happened; your description must paint an honest picture of the situation. If you're angry when you draft your claim letter, let several hours pass before you revise, edit, and send it. When your anger subsides, you'll write a more effective message.

Use concrete terms. *Big gash* says less than *4″ × 1″* tear. Enclose copies of purchase orders, invoices, shipping lists, or other documents related to the claim. Include photos of the damage if you have them. Put yourself in the reader's position. What would you need to know to respond positively to the claim?

## CHECKPOINT 4-3

## CONTROLLING ANGER, PART 2

Refer to the situation described in Checkpoint 4-2. What information would you advise Jordan to include in the **middle** of his claim message?

If the action you want is not stated in the opening, you must describe it in the closing. Businesses appreciate writers who tell them what they want, as long as the request is reasonable. Threats (withholding business; publicizing the problem) or unreasonable demands (asking for a year's supply of cola because one can in a 12-pack was empty) can make the reader defensive and unsympathetic to your claim.

Getting what you ask for may require information from the reader. In the close, you might ask what to do with damaged goods, how to return merchandise, and who will pay the shipping costs.

The closing should build goodwill. Be gracious and sincere. Avoid overworked statements such as *Thank you for your prompt attention to this matter.*

## CONTROLLING ANGER, PART 3

Review the situation described in Checkpoint 4-2. Write the **closing** to the message.

A complete claim letter is shown in Figure 4-3. This message uses a subject line to introduce the topic and provide information related to the claim.

# @ % & ! # $ % @ & % $

**Figures cited in "Strive for Perfection—OR ELSE!" indicate that:**

- **811,000 faulty rolls of 35mm film will be loaded this year.**
- **22,000 checks will be deducted from the wrong bank accounts in the next 60 minutes.**
- **2,488,200 books with the wrong cover will be shipped in the next 12 months.**
- **880,000 credit cards in circulation will turn out to have incorrect cardholder information on their magnetic strips.**
- **5,517,200 cases of soft drinks produced in the next 12 months will be flatter than a bad tire.**

**Each situation could be treated as a valid claim.**

**The Treasure Chest**

Towne Plaza • 809 Milford Road
Cheyenne, WY 82001-4568

March 12, 20—

Paxton Products, Inc.
Box 3840-J
Mount Vermon, OR 97865-3840

**DAMAGED MERCHANDISE—Invoice 2312**

Three of the twelve music boxes contained in the shipment received
March 11 were broken.

When the package was delivered, our clerk noticed that one corner was crushed.
The clerk commented about the condition of the package but was told by the
carrier's representative that claims should be made to the shipper. When the
clerk opened the box to examine its contents, she found the broken music boxes.
Please replace the following merchandise:

| ITEM | DESCRIPTION/TUNE | CONDITION |
|------|------------------|-----------|
| 245-CL | Sad Clown/Send in the Clowns | base shattered |
| 245-RA | Rabbit/Here Comes Peter Cottontail | ear missing |
| 245-RO | Rosebud/Anniversary Waltz | petals cracked |

The damaged items are being returned to you c.o.d. We are confident that you
will replace them by April 15 so that we will have them for our spring sale.

JANICE GRUDER
MANAGER

**Figure 4-3**
Claim Letter

✛ European business writers may be even more direct than those
in the U.S. When asked to respond to a list of questions, a typical
European reply might be "Yes. Yes. £16 per unit. Two weeks."

*Chapter 4: Writing Positive and Neutral News Messages*

# WRITING REPLIES

Every message that asks a question, makes a request, places an order, or makes a claim deserves a response, but not all responses need to be formal messages. A preprinted message form that says *This note is sent to ensure a prompt reply* is one option. Another possibility is to stamp *Quick Reply* on the incoming letter or memo and write your response right on the message. Reader analysis will help you determine whether informality is appropriate. If you use an informal method, make and retain a photocopy of the document before you send it.

When your analysis of the receiver and situation shows that a formal memo or letter is required, use the direct approach. This approach will serve you well as you write inquiry responses, request approvals, order acknowledgments, and claim adjustments.

## Inquiry Responses

Begin your message with the information the writer wants or with a statement that introduces a vertical list of responses. Receiving the good news in the opening will encourage the receiver and motivate him or her to read the details. Omit openings such as *Your letter regarding xxx has been received.* The reader knows this; why else would you be writing?

In the middle of the message, give complete responses to questions the reader has asked. Don't add unnecessary details as it wastes your time and could annoy the reader. If a shipment is late because of a factory fire, the reader doesn't care about where the factory is located, when the fire took place, or other details. The reader only wants to know when the shipment will be made.

End with a courteous, forward-looking statement that sounds fresh and sincere. *Write again if we can help on a future project* is better than *If you have additional questions, please do not hesitate to contact us.* The letter in Figure 4-4 on page 76 presents one possible response to the inquiry in Figure 4-1.

## Request Approvals

Approve requests by presenting the good news first: *Yes! You and your Junior Achievement group may tour our production facility on October 29.* The pleasure associated with knowing the request has been approved will motivate the reader to learn what must be done next.

The middle of the message gives important information. The detail section should be clear and complete. If details are unclear, the reader won't understand. If details are incomplete, additional communication will be needed. A positive close comes after the details.

Bangor Tourism Office
987 Babcock Trail
Bangor, ME 04402-1174

March 11, 20—

Blake Amroke
5768 East 7th Avenue
Monroe, LA 71201-3371

Dear Mr. Amroke:

As you requested, we are enclosing the following items:

- Maps for the city of Bangor and the downtown area.

- A brochure that lists several area lodging facilities and the amenities they offer.

- Brochures describing parks, recreational facilities, shopping, and cultural sites in Bangor and Penobscot County.

- A list of special events occurring in our area during June and July.

Our office is located in downtown Bangor—we've marked it for you on the map. Stop in during your visit, and we'll tell you more about the area. You may also wish to consult our website at http://www.bairnet.org/municipal. There you'll find links to various communities and activities.

We're looking forward to sharing the beauty of Maine with you this summer.

Sincerely,


Adeline Wilcox, Tourism Director

Enclosures

**Figure 4-4**
Inquiry Response

# Order Acknowledgments or Confirmations

Because customers are more interested in receiving their merchandise than in reading about their order, acknowledgments and confirmations are not always sent. This is especially true for direct mail businesses that have many one-time customers or repeat customers who buy infrequently. When organizations do acknowledge orders, a pre-printed or computer generated card is convenient. The card may list the items and the shipping date or just a statement like *Your order is being prepared for shipment; you should receive it within two weeks.*

*Routine order acknowledgments or confirmations are informal.*

Special circumstances call for a formal response. The first order from a new customer, a large order from a regular customer, a shipment that must be delayed, or an order that can't be filled completely are examples of special circumstances that require a formal response.

If an order acknowledgment or confirmation has good and bad news, use the direct approach and present the good news first. Tell the reader what will be delivered on time, explain why some items will be delivered late, and stress when the reader can expect to receive the late shipment. Placing the explanation in an introductory dependent clause helps emphasize the good news in the independent clause that follows. *Although floods in the Red River Valley have temporarily halted production of the Rapid Cut 330 in our region, your order is receiving priority at our West Region plant. Your shipment should reach you by May 1.*

**Resale** or **promotional** information can be added to order acknowledgments and confirmations. Resale statements highlight one or two of the product's features or reassure readers that their purchase was a good one. Promotional statements describe new or related products and services.

The closing of an acknowledgment letter expresses appreciation and a desire to continue the business relationship. *We appreciate the confidence you have in us, Mrs. Whitehall. You can always count on our high-quality products and reliable service.*

> *Mixed news messages use the direct approach, with the good news first.*

> *Promotional or resale material may be incorporated into a reply message.*

> *Make positive remarks about the future in the close.*

## CHECKPOINT 4-5

### ACKNOWLEDGING AN ORDER

Write an opening to be used in a letter from a flower wholesaler who wants to acknowledge an order for 100 dozen roses. This is the first time the customer has ordered flowers from this wholesaler.

## Claim Adjustments

Businesses have ethical and legal obligations to make adjustments for valid claims against their products and services. However, it is not the fear of legal action that encourages businesses to process claims efficiently and effectively. It is the desire to serve their customers. Good customer service can produce repeat business. Handling claims to the satisfaction of customers leads to good word-of-mouth advertising. Relying on customer feedback can lead to better products or services.

So much is gained by adjusting claims satisfactorily that businesses do so routinely. Most medium to large firms have consumer affairs or customer relations departments to handle the task. Unless a claim is clearly bogus or the requested adjustment is outrageous, companies will usually settle the claim quickly and happily.

Claim adjustment messages are often form letters. The core of each message is filed electronically then retrieved and personalized to the customer and the situation. Figure 4-5 shows a claim adjustment form letter.

The letter uses the direct approach: The opening says what claim is being adjusted, the middle gives details and tries to restore customer confidence, and the close encourages repeat business.

Most writers believe apologies do more harm than good because they can be construed as an admission of guilt. If used late in the message, apologies remind the reader of the problem and diminish goodwill.

The tone and word choice of adjustment letters are very important. The tone must be polite without being condescending. The situation must be explained without placing blame. Confidence should be restored without promising that the situation will never happen again.

# WRITING UNSOLICITED INFORMATION MESSAGES

*Claims help organizations provide better products and services.*

*Choose words carefully; avoid apologies unless absolutely necessary.*

*Many business messages are unsolicited by the reader; they are designed simply to inform.*

Many of the messages distributed within an organization are unsolicited. Their purpose is to inform rather than to respond to questions or requests. These messages, sent as e-mails or memos, contain information needed to conduct work in the organization. Because informational messages are routine, writers expect readers to have a neutral or positive reaction. The messages are, therefore, organized by the direct approach. The following text, sent by e-mail, is an example:

✦ This passage from a business memo was printed in the "Doublespeak" feature of *The Winner's Circle.*

"A spot-check of randomly selected directories indicated that a number of the directories contained several blank pages. In view of the foregoing it is suggested that each user review the issued directory and ascertain whether or not the directory is complete. In the event the directory is incomplete, the user should return the directory to issue source for disposition."

*Translation:* If your directory has blank pages, send it back to me.

*Chapter 4: Writing Positive and Neutral News Messages*

Two early morning power surges caused a loss of long distance telephone service. We expect to have the switch repaired by noon today.

Informational messages also can be sent to external audiences. Office relocations, deadline extensions, calls for bids and proposals, routine billing notices, and reports from subcontractors to contractors illustrate some of these communications. Other internal messages that would be categorized as unsolicited and positive or neutral involve policies and procedures.

---

## COAR Company

PO Box 572
Overland Park, KS 66211-2247

November 27, 20—

Dear Customer:

Thank you for telling us about your experience with COAR's Chicken Fettucini frozen dinner. You deserve the highest products when you buy COAR, and we strive to ensure you get them.

Our Quality Assurance staff has examined the material you sent and identified it as vegetable residue, which may have entered our plant with the raw ingredients.

Because of the very rigid quality control standards and the precaution we observe throughout the production cycle, we are concerned when foreign materials find their way into our products. You may be assured that prompt action will be taken on this matter and that we will take steps to prevent similar incidents from occurring in the future.

Please accept the enclosed coupons as a token of our appreciation for your interest in keeping the quality of COAR products high. We trust that you will again try our products and find them to be delicious, nutritious, and convenient.

Sincerely,

Melvin Patronas, Consumer Affairs Manager

Enclosures

**Figure 4-5**
Claim Response

# CHAPTER SUMMARY

♦ Use the direct approach when you expect readers will have a positive or neutral reaction to your message.

♦ The direct approach has the following parts:

An opening that focuses on the main idea—the good news.

A middle that provides details to support the main idea.

A positive close that generates goodwill.

♦ Use the direct approach when writing the following messages and positive responses to them:

inquiries

requests

routine claims

routine informational messages

♦ Vertical lists attract attention and help writers and readers.

**words@work** Go to the Writing Tab; access and read the lesson on Business Letters. Complete the appropriate *words@work* exercises.

# CHAPTER 4 APPLICATIONS

**SECTION I** *Work-related Messages.* The following exercises require you to apply the direct approach. Read the directions carefully. Unless specified in the text or by your instructor, choose the memo/letter style you prefer (refer to Appendix A). Apply the 4Cs of communication covered in Chapter 3, and remember to proofread your messages for content and mechanics.

1. You manage the chemical stockroom at Enterprise Pharmaceuticals. Chemicals are purchased and stored centrally. Departments are billed for whatever they use. It is your job to tell employees that on the first of next month the stockroom hours will change from 1–3 PM to 9–11 AM. Most of Enterprise's shipments arrive in the afternoon, and shifting the stockroom hours will allow your staff to do an inventory and shelve the new stock without interruption. You're willing to fill requests that arrive in the afternoon, but a 15 percent markup will be added.

   Plan your communication by answering the following questions:

   a. Who will read your message?

   b. Through what medium will you distribute the message? Why did you select this method?

   c. What is the main idea?

   d. What details must you include?

   e. Are readers required to reply? If so, how? By when?

   f. What positive thought would you use to close the message?

   g. Are enclosures needed? If so, what?

Using the notes you made in items a-g, write the message at the top of the next page.

Write your message here:

2. When you arrived at work this morning, you found a note from your supervisor (Suzanne Samkoff, Office Services Department Manager) asking you to *"Finish, edit, sign, and send this. We need to know how many they want and where to deliver them. You'll process the requests as we receive them."* Do as Suzanne asks.

All Admin. Support Staff

The new editions of the corporate style manual have arrived! The manual offers the latest newest information about the letter, punctuation, memo and envelope styles used here at Titan Industries. It also dispenses priceless information about in-house reprographics services and proposes numerous suggestions on how we can economize—time and dollars. How can YOU get a copy of this worthwhile

3. The "Tidbits" section of the March issue of *Today's Technology* contained the following entry:

SSI has announced a new program that automates the scheduling process. Users input their staffing needs for each hour of the week. MORETIME matches them to worker lists and produces a schedule. One Chicago clothing store that used the system cut overstaffed hours by 85% and reduced understaffed hours by 58%. After just two weeks of testing, managers refused to schedule manually any longer.

You manage the home furnishings department of Old Oak department store. You believe MORETIME would benefit your store. After reading "Tidbits," you phoned a local computer store to ask about the software. The clerk said the store didn't stock MORETIME and that she wasn't familiar with it. She was able, however, to tell you that SSI's mailing address is Suite 401-A, Blaine Building, 1200 Artistic Way, Anaheim, CA 92805-1200. Prepare an appropriate message.

4. Refer to Exercise 3. You received the desired response from SSI. Old Oak's department managers meet the second Tuesday of each month. The store manager sets the agenda for department managers' meetings. You'd like the group to spend 10–15 minutes discussing the possibility of buying the software. Prepare and send an appropriate e-mail message to the manager (your instructor).

*Chapter 4: Writing Positive and Neutral News Messages*

5. You work in your state's Department of Revenue office. The tax code for your state permits residents to file for a property tax rebate, but as many as 2,000 residents fail to do so each year. The department has used income tax and property tax records to calculate the appropriate rebate and has issued checks to these residents. Prepare a form letter to accompany the check.

6. Your supervisor has asked you to notify the members of the budget committee that the meeting scheduled for 10 AM next Monday has been rescheduled for 2 PM Thursday of the following week. The site has also changed to Room 312. The change is because of a delay in getting a tax ruling from the IRS. No new items will be added to the agenda. Write the message and e-mail it to your instructor.

7. You work for a mail order firm whose ads are published in newspapers throughout the country. One of your most popular products, a coupon holder, is out of stock. Prepare the text of a message that will be printed on a postcard and sent to customers who have ordered the product. You expect delivery to be delayed about four weeks.

8. Your company has decided to issue photo ID badges to its employees. Effective July 1, employees must show their badge to gain entry to areas beyond the lobby. Your supervisor has given you the job of coordinating the photo sessions.

   a. Prepare a message to be sent to the employees of your firm. Cameras will be set up in Conference Room A from 8:30 AM to 4 PM each weekday from June 1 through 12. Appointments aren't necessary. Workers should bring a completed information card with them. Badges will be distributed by the end of the month.

   b. It's May 25. Prepare a message to the department secretaries in your company asking them to remind workers about the photo sessions. Send your message to your instructor.

   c. Write to the photographer, Paul Peterson, to confirm the sessions. When you spoke with him last week, Paul said he preferred to leave his equipment in or near the room where photos are to be taken. There's a closet in the conference room. The closet and the room can be locked each evening. He may leave his equipment there, but you assume no liability for damage or theft.

9. For the past 10 years, full-time employees of your firm have been entitled to a 10 percent discount on the products you produce. The Board of Directors agreed to increase the discount to 15 percent on credit card purchases and to 20 percent on cash purchases. Part-time workers will receive a 10 percent discount on cash purchases only. As an administrative assistant to Barbara Medina, Chair of the Board, you will draft a message to the employees telling them about the policy change.

10. You are office manager for an independent insurance agency. The small community in which you work doesn't have an office products store, so you order supplies from mail-order companies that send catalogs to your office. Today you received a shipment containing eight boxes of five-cut orange file folders designed for traditional filing cabinets. You checked your files and confirmed that the order you placed three weeks ago was for eight boxes of manila file folders to be used with your open-shelf filing system. You know that the cost of shipping your order will be included in your bill, but you don't believe you should pay shipping costs for returning the wrong merchandise. Write a message to be included with the folders you return.

11. You work in the administrative services division of a large bank. Six months ago your company started a paper recycling program. Each employee was given a small cardboard container and encouraged to use it instead of a waste basket. Employees empty their individual containers into larger bins, and the refuse is bundled and recycled.

The program has been more successful than anyone expected. Nearly two tons of paper have been recycled, and the company's waste removal costs have dropped 14 percent. Prepare a message thanking employees for their cooperation and encouraging them to continue to recycle. E-mail your message to your instructor.

12. You work for the firm that manages the Heritage Mall. In response to the increased interest in health and exercise, your firm has decided to open the mall at 7 AM instead of 9 AM Health-conscious people who like early-morning exercise can walk in comfort and safety and "window shop" until the stores open at 9:30 AM Walkers will be told to use the north entry. Shops will continue to open at 9:30 AM. Prepare a message to be sent to the merchants who rent space in your mall.

13. You are the customer service representative at Rapid Copy Printers. Yesterday you received the following letter from a regular customer, Baker Cabinets:

OOPS!

Three of the 12 boxes of envelopes delivered March 15 (Invoice No. 18664-2) contained the incorrect logo and return address.

When the order arrived, our clerk opened one box and checked the first envelope for accuracy. Finding no problem, the clerk signed the receipt and shelved the boxes. Today, when the envelopes were distributed to users, we noticed that two of the boxes contained envelopes bearing the logo and return address of Chaffee Investments. A sample is enclosed.

Please send us two boxes of envelopes imprinted with our logo and return address. Also, let us know what you would like us to do with Chaffee's envelopes.

MARK NOYES
PURCHASING AGENT

Enclosure

On a separate sheet of paper, write a response to this letter. Approve the claim. Chaffee's envelopes should be destroyed. Two boxes of correctly imprinted envelopes should reach them by March 30. Two desk calendars will be included in the shipment at no charge.

14. Your office has a "sunshine" fund. The money pays for the cards and flowers sent to workers to recognize occasions such as weddings, births, graduations, illnesses, or deaths. After paying the bill you received today, you have only $14.95 in the fund. It's time to ask for contributions. Prepare a message to be circulated to the 30 people in your office. (Would it be appropriate to suggest a minimum amount?)

15. You are a sales associate in a furniture store that stocks expensive merchandise. A lamp, for example, could cost as much as $500. Each sale generates a commission for you. Prepare a form letter to customers who make purchases from you. Personalize this message so these customers will ask for you the next time they shop at your store.

16. Beth and Ben Hilager asked your company to sponsor the local youth soccer team they coach. Sponsorship includes paying a $75 City League entry fee and furnishing printed t-shirts for the players. If you sponsor a team, you can choose a name for it. You know from experience that some sponsors also contribute money toward post-game refreshments and an end-of-season banquet. Prepare an appropriate response to the request.

17. You prepare taxes in an accounting firm. Each spring, as you get ready for the tax season, you send your clients a worksheet that outlines the figures you used to prepare their taxes the previous year. If the clients take the time to complete the worksheet showing the income/expenses they incurred during the current tax year, the billable time devoted to preparing their taxes is greatly reduced. Prepare the letter urging them to complete and return the worksheet promptly.

18. You are an insurance agent. Last night, your area was struck by a tremendous storm. The 4" rainfall was bad enough, but the 40 mph winds and baseball-size hail were the real problem. Many of your policyholders' homes and cars were damaged. You've worked with your regional office and identified four contractors who will work with you to do home repair estimates. In addition, you've arranged to have a satellite auto assessment center established in the parking lot of a local office building. Write your clients providing them with appropriate information.

19. Access the Web site at URL *http://www.bbb.org* and find the Better Business Bureau that serves your area. Write a memo to your instructor summarizing what the BBB does.

20. Access the Web site at URL *http://www.plainlanguage.gov* or another Web site that discusses plain language laws. In a memo, summarize the information contained at the site or on one of its links.

**SECTION II** *Personal Business Messages.* The following exercises relate to using the direct approach in writing situations you might face in your personal life. Read the directions carefully. Select a style that is appropriate for a personal business message (refer to Appendix A). Apply the 4Cs of good communication presented in Chapter 3. Plan before you write, and proofread for content and mechanics.

21. The Business Leaders group at the high school you attended has invited you to speak at its annual awards banquet on May 12. Their invitation says they want you to give a 15-minute presentation on a topic of your choice. The event will be held in the Empire Room of the Imperial Hotel. Dinner will be served at 7 PM and the program will begin at 8. Your spouse or a guest may attend with you.

    Prepare a letter that accepts the invitation. You were a member of the club for three years and welcome the chance to return. Tell them the career-related topic you have selected and that you will attend alone.

22. You and two friends spent last weekend in another city. You arrived home late Sunday night, unpacked your suitcase, and discovered that your travel alarm clock was missing. You called your friends, but none of them have it, so you must have left it on the bedstand in your hotel room. You phoned the hotel but were unable to learn whether the clock had been found. The desk clerk advised you to write to Ramona DeAngeles, housekeeping supervisor for the hotel. Do as the clerk advised.

23. You got home from work late last night and weren't in the mood to cook a full meal, so you decided to prepare a box of macaroni and cheese. When you opened the box, you found pasta but no cheese. Frustrated, you ordered a pizza and vowed that today you would write to the company. Write an appropriate claim message.

24. You are a member of several clubs and professional associations. Prepare the text of a message that could be sent to these groups notifying them that you are moving.

25. You are looking for a new job. Write to ask a current/former teacher or employer to be a reference for you.

# WRITING BAD NEWS MESSAGES

Entrepreneurs face many obstacles when trying to launch a business, not the least of which is securing financial backing for their projects. One such individual was Debbi Fields, who at age 20 tried to get capital to start a cookie store. According to the Famous Last Words web site (http://web.mit.edu/randy/www/words/html), Mrs. Fields was told by one potential funder "A cookie store is a bad idea. Besides, the market research reports say America likes crispy cookies, not soft and chewy cookies like you make." We know now that the person who conveyed this bad news to Mrs. Fields missed a tremendous investment opportunity. After reading this chapter, you'll also know how the message sender could have conveyed the bad news more tactfully.

## TYPES OF BAD NEWS MESSAGES

Bad news messages can be classified into three types—*request refusals*, *adjustment refusals*, and *unexpected bad news*. Request and adjustment refusals respond to messages from customers, employees, or others. Unexpected bad news arises from decisions made within the organization. These decisions must be conveyed to those affected by them.

## THE INDIRECT APPROACH

Most people dislike giving bad news almost as much as they dislike receiving it. Despite the dislike for it, bad news is a reality in business. Because bad news can't be avoided, writers soften it by using the indirect approach.

### Why the Indirect Approach Works

The **indirect approach** is based on psychology. The first aspect of psychology relates to location in the message. Writers know that first and last positions have the greatest emphasis. They do not put bad news at the start or end of a message or paragraph. A receiver might not read the entire

### LEARNING OBJECTIVES

- Identify the three types of bad news messages.
- Explain the features of the indirect organizational plan and know when it should be used to convey bad news.
- Recognize when it is appropriate to use the direct plan to organize bad news messages.
- Compose effective bad news messages.
- Select a distribution method appropriate to messages that convey bad news.

*The three types of bad news messages are:*
- *Request Refusals*
- *Adjustment Refusals*
- *Unexpected Bad News*

message if the bad news is put first. Yet, the rest of the message contains important information about *why* the news is bad.

Another psychological link concerns space. People equate space with importance. The more space devoted to an idea, the more important it will seem. Writers minimize bad news by limiting it to one sentence or to a clause within a sentence. Because a one-sentence paragraph is emphatic, however, that display is not used for bad news.

People's reading patterns are also psychological factors. Writers know that people tend to start at the top of a message and will read to the end only if their interest can be held. By delaying the bad news, writers hold the interest of their readers.

Finally, writers acknowledge that readers may never *like* receiving bad news. Therefore, they try to get receivers to *accept* that they were treated fairly and that the decision was not arbitrary or mean spirited. When this acceptance occurs, the relationship between the sender and receiver will stay strong and goodwill will be saved.

## Parts of Bad News Indirect Messages

A bad news message organized by the indirect approach has five sections: *buffer, explanation, bad news, counterproposal/resale,* and *close.* Bad news is placed in the middle of the message. The placement is strategic, not deceptive. The following paragraphs describe the sections of the bad news message.

THE BUFFER. Bad news messages begin with a buffer. A **buffer** is a statement related to the *topic* of the message but unrelated to the bad news. Its gets the reader into the message without indicating whether good or bad news follows. The buffer softens the impact of the bad news.

A buffer may be positive or neutral. Positive buffers are used when some aspect of the situation is favorable. For example, a positive buffer would be used when part of an order can be delivered and part will be delayed. If no part of the order is available, the buffer would be neutral. A buffer should be brief. A long buffer may suggest that the writer is avoiding something and make the reader suspicious.

A good buffer does not indicate whether a request is being approved or denied. It contains an apology only when the writer is at fault. Here's an example:

> Your October 7 letter describing the problem you are having with your Springer Lawn Trimmer has been referred to me. I apologize for not responding to your letter sooner.

In this buffer, the writer is apologizing for not responding quickly, not for the request denial that will come later. The difference is subtle, but important. Note, too, that the writer did not thank the receiver for his or her message. Gratitude should be used sparingly and cautiously in bad news messages because its meaning could be misinterpreted. Are you thanking the person because you enjoy saying "no"?

*The indirect approach uses psychology with regard to:*
- *location*
- *space*
- *reading patterns*
- *acceptance versus pleasure*

*Bad news messages organized indirectly have five sections.*

*The buffer cushions the blow.*

*Buffers may be positive or neutral.*

*Use apologies sparingly.*

*Chapter 5: Writing Bad News Messages*

Buffers should not mislead the reader. A writer who, trying to be positive, says *"Thank you for your order and request for credit. We have been impressed by your success and know that you have a bright future"* builds the reader's confidence that good news follows. When readers learn the news is bad, they may be confused or become angry and resist the explanation.

## CHECKPOINT 5-1

### ANALYZING BUFFERS

Are the following buffers strong or weak? Why?

Thank you for your memo, Maxine; it's always a pleasure to hear from a hard-working, loyal employee.

We've reviewed your request for warranty repair to your refrigerator. Unfortunately, the warranty expired two months ago.

Seung, it was good to get your e-mail. It's been quite a while since we in Payroll have heard from you or any of the other people in the Safety Division. I hear you've put together a strong team for this year's summer softball league!

As you requested, your video camera has been checked. Our technicians have determined that the camera requires a minor adjustment and replacement of only one part.

A good buffer introduces the topic without revealing the bad news and forms a natural bridge to what follows—an explanation or reasons for the bad news.

THE EXPLANATION. The explanation is usually the longest part of the message. In this section, the writer clearly and honestly presents information designed to get the reader to accept the bad news that will follow.

As you prepare the transition from the buffer to the explanation, choose your words carefully. Transitional words such as *unfortunately* and *however* signal bad news or a change from the positive/neutral tone

# "You're all really great, except for **60** or **70** little things."

**WORKPLACE CONNECTIONS**

If you have difficulty finding the right words to write bad news messages, try to visualize your reader and speak as though she/he were seated beside you. Then, write what you said.

*The explanation presents your reasons.*

*Respect your receiver.*

of the opening to bad news. Another word to avoid is *but*. Think about how you feel when you ask someone to do something and the response is, "I'd like to help you, but. . . ." Your reader will feel the same disappointment.

A good explanation shows how the specific reader, or customers/employees in general, will benefit. For example, *Participants are guaranteed personal attention when the trainer:student ratio is held at 12:1* shows concern for providing a high-quality learning environment. An explanation such as *We can't afford to* is writer centered and money focused. An explanation such as *It's against our policy* is unclear. Weak explanations can cause reader resentment. What is the policy? Why does it exist? Be specific.

Only one *good* reason is required. Include additional reasons if they will increase reader goodwill and acceptance of the bad news without destroying the brevity of the message. Stretching for reasons can weaken the explanation. As part of the planning process, the writer should list and prioritize the reasons for saying no. If the reasons cannot be listed or if they are not convincing, reevaluate the negative decision or action.

Be careful, too, not to insult the reader. Condescending language such as *Surely you understand*, *You claim*, or *We have never had a request like this before* will make the reader defensive.

By the time the receiver has read the buffer and the explanation, he/she should not be surprised by what follows—the bad news.

THE BAD NEWS. Bad news may be implied or expressed. **Implied** bad news hints at the *no*. **Expressed** bad news is more specific. If you must use negative words, choose them carefully. Be tactful, not blunt. Base your choice of implied or expressed bad news on your analysis of the receiver. In general, implied bad news is preferred. Notice in the following example that the same item of bad news can be implied or expressed.

Implied: Paid leaves of absence are available only to employees who have been with the company for one year or more.

Expressed: Paid leaves of absence are available only to employees who have been with the company for one year or more. Because you began working at Goodhue only three months ago, you are not yet eligible for a paid leave of absence.

> "If someone tells you he is going to make a 'realistic decision,' you immediately understand that he has resolved to do something bad."
>
> **Mary McCarthy**

*Bad news may be implied or expressed.*

> **❝ Focus on remedies, not faults. ❞**
>
> Jack Nicklaus

Recall from your study of emphasis techniques that a one-sentence paragraph is emphatic. Since writers want to minimize the emphasis on the bad news, they often link it to the explanation or to the counterproposal/resale section.

**THE COUNTERPROPOSAL/RESALE.** The **counterproposal** is a valuable section of a bad news message. It is the place where the writer shows genuine concern for and interest in helping the receiver. It is where the writer says, "I can't do what (or everything) you ask, but here's what I will do." The counterproposal should be reasonable, as in this example:

> Although you don't qualify for credit, you are eligible for a discount when you pay cash.

The counterproposal should be stated positively and clearly. It should provide all details the reader needs to take action. Provide names, addresses, phone numbers, dates, costs, figures, and other information; include a reply card or brochure as appropriate. Make the communication as complete as possible.

As previously noted, writers try to minimize the impact of bad news by linking it to the explanation or to the counterproposal/resale section. When linked to the counterproposal, the bad news is typically presented as a dependent clause. Here is an example:

> Although your practical work experience is too limited for you to become a finalist for the accounts manager position, the account associate position we have available seems to suit you well. The position calls for a self-motivated, energetic person who has at least one year of post-secondary accounting education and familiarity with information systems.

**Resale** is used in situations where a counterproposal is impossible or impractical. Resale material is designed to maintain or build goodwill between the sender and receiver. For example, a message to scholarship applicants who were not selected to receive an award doesn't offer an opportunity for a counterproposal. A statement or two about some particular strength of the candidate's background would be appropriate. The statement(s) would be considered resale because they make the reader feel good about himself or herself and about the scholarship organization. Here is an example:

> The selection committee was very impressed by your career goals and your strong work experience. You can be proud of your accomplishments.

*Chapter 5: Writing Bad News Messages*

Coupons or discounts on future purchases are additional examples of resale. If neither a counterproposal nor resale material is appropriate, include additional reasons for the decision. Any of the three will help minimize the bad news. Once this section has been presented, it is time to close the message.

THE POSITIVE, FRIENDLY CLOSE.  Because the last position in a message is prominent, writers want to end with a positive, friendly close. Any reference to the bad news, no matter how well meaning the writer may be, merely reminds the receiver about it. Referring to the bad news defeats the efforts that went into de-emphasizing it.

The **close** may relate to the reader, the counterproposal, or the business relationship between the sender and receiver—anything that is *on* the topic but *off* the bad news. Choose words carefully. Avoid words that show doubt (*hope, if* ) and words that are negative (*problem, condition, situation*).

*Be optimistic in the close.*

## CHECKPOINT 5-4

## CLOSINGS

Are the following closings strong or weak? Why?

Thanks again for writing. The next time you have this problem, please call us again.

Call 1-800-555-0939 to order your repair kit.

Please greet your family for me.

I'm sorry I can't help you, Marsha, but the policy must be enforced.

# APPLYING THE INDIRECT APPROACH TO BUSINESS BAD NEWS MESSAGES

Now that the parts of the indirect bad news message have been explained, it is time to examine how they can be combined to form messages.

> ✛ "You send out letters, you get back letters, that's for sure!" says Lazlo Toth, who in real life is Don Novello, otherwise known as Father Guido Sarducci of Saturday Night Live. Acting as Lazlo Toth, Novello wrote letters to various corporations and individuals. Toth's letters were often tongue-in-cheek suggestions (a theme song for President Nixon) or queries (How do you use bubble bath powder when "keep dry" is printed on the box?) The replies, however, were mostly courteous and helpful; often, they were organized indirectly. The letters and responses are presented in The Lazlo Letters; 1976, revised 1992; Workman Publishing Company, New York.

*Request refusals follow the indirect approach.*

## Request Refusals

Customer and employee requests—invitations, orders, credit applications, or correspondence related to policy—are taken very seriously. Also taken seriously are the messages written when these requests must be refused. Because customer and employee satisfaction are important to business success, writers use the indirect approach when refusing their requests.

Request refusals should begin with a buffer that relates to the receiver and/or the request. Next, give the reason(s) for the refusal. The explanation should focus on the receiver or be neutral. The reader may recognize that the decision also benefits the writer, but the writer should not stress this gain. The bad news, presented after the explanation for it, may be either expressed or implied. A counterproposal and a positive, friendly closing complete the message.

Assume that Pam Saljak, who works as an inventory clerk at Quality Restaurant Supply, has requested that she be considered for a 5 percent salary increase. Pam, a single mother of two, recently purchased an older home and has indicated that the home needs a new roof and some cosmetic updates. Pam has worked at QRS for about five years; her performance has been consistently rated as outstanding. In fact, during the annual performance review conducted just three months ago, Pam earned higher ratings than anyone else in her department. Her supervisor faces the challenge of keeping Pam's morale high while telling her a raise won't be awarded. Figure 5-1 presents one way to respond to Pam's request.

Notice that the buffer is an accurate statement of what has happened but that it does not indicate whether the request is being approved or denied. The explanation describes the company's policy and shows how it benefits the receiver and other employees. The bad news is expressed and linked to the counterproposal. The positive, friendly close spins naturally from the counterproposal. In addition, it stresses Pam's record of service, hard work, and loyalty.

**MEMO**

TO:         Pam Salijak

FROM:       Linc Whitlock

DATE:       March 23, 20—

SUBJECT:    **SALARY INCREASE**

**1** Pam, your request for a salary increase has been received and carefully considered.

**2** QRS wants to ensure that each employee receives individual attention and that the time between evaluations is the same for every worker. Therefore, cost-of-living raises are awarded in January and merit increase reviews are conducted during each employee's anniversary month.

**3** Because you received a 3 percent cost-of-living raise in January and will be reviewed for a merit increase in July, your request to be considered for a salary increase at this time is denied. The Quality Employee Credit Union (QECU) may, however, be of help to you in meeting your remodeling needs. Home improvement loans are currently being offered at a low 7.6 percent interest rate. In addition, QECU maintains listings of carpenters and other craftspeople who do quality work at reasonable rates.

**4** Pam, QECU serves all Quality Restaurant Service employees who have been with the firm for at least six months; a $25 deposit is all that's necessary to establish membership. You've been a hard-working, loyal employee for nearly five years. To learn more about the services offered by the Credit Union, call 555-1234 or speak with the representative in Room 225, Building K.

## Annotations

1. Buffer

2. Explanation

3. Bad News and Counterproposal

4. Positive, Friendly Close

**Figure 5-1**
Request Refusal

### RESALE

Assume that Pam Saljak did not tell her supervisor why she wanted a raise. Prepare a resale paragraph that could be used in place of the counterproposal.

---

*Claims are denied using the indirect approach.*

## Adjustment Refusals

In Chapter 4, you learned that claims are viewed as good news because they give the organization an opportunity to redeem itself, identify and correct problems, and promote goodwill. Unfortunately, not all claims are valid. Some claims reflect consumer negligence, some ask for extraordinary remedies, and some are frivolous or simply false.

One highly publicized false claim occurred in 1993 when a man in Tacoma, Washington, claimed to have found a syringe in a can of Diet Pepsi. Within days, other customers reported finding everything from needles to bullets in their sodas. The claim turned out to be a product-tampering hoax that resulted in arrests, but it reportedly cost the company nearly $15 million in sales in just one week.

Very few claims create this type of crisis for an organization. The case does illustrate that companies receive both valid and invalid claims. If a business is to be profitable and maintain its integrity, it must honor valid claims and refuse all others. The indirect approach is used for messages written in response to claims that are denied.

Adjustment refusals begin with a buffer that relates to the topic but not the bad news. Next, the writer presents reasons for the refusal. Facts are more convincing than opinions. If an investigation was conducted or tests run, say so. The results are the foundation for the bad news.

Receiver viewpoint must be considered when writing the explanation. Therefore, writers often use passive rather than active voice. For example:

*Passive voice can temper negative news.*

Active Voice:   You dropped the clock.
Passive Voice:  The clock has been dropped.

Give the bad news in implied or expressed terms. Avoid using words like *grant* and *allow*. They suggest that the writer has power and that the gap between the status of the sender and receiver is large. If possible, offer a counterproposal; otherwise, include a resale statement. End pleasantly. A closing encouraging the reader to act on the counterproposal is positive.

*Avoid words that emphasize the writer's power.*

Remember, word-of-mouth advertising is very powerful. The manner in which claims are handled affects the way claimants view writers and their organizations. If customers are satisfied with the way a claim is handled, *even when it is refused,* they are apt to speak well of the organization. They will become informal goodwill ambassadors for the organization.

Assume that Alyson Chambers has requested that the electric wok she purchased one month ago be repaired without charge. She states: "The first time I used the wok it worked well. When I went to use it last night, however, the wok wouldn't heat. I don't understand why. All I did was use it, clean it, and put it away." Your technician inspected the heating element and quickly discovered the problem. The element had gotten wet—something the owner's manual warns against. Figure 5-2 presents a bad news response to the claim.

Notice that the adjustment refusal in Figure 5-2 introduces the topic in the subject line. Doing so allows the writer to develop the buffer around the idea that the heating element is vital to successful wok cookery. The explanation section presents the findings in a nonaccusatory manner and states clearly that the warranty is no longer in effect. The counterproposal offers the reader two options, and the closing makes action easy. The statement about wok cooking being healthy cooking links the closing paragraph to the opening paragraph and enhances the overall unity of the message.

*A subject line can be useful in introducing the topic of a message.*

# Annotations

1. Buffer

2. Reasons

3. Bad News

4. Counterproposal

5. Positive, "Action" Close

**Major Electric Company**
4568 Highway J • Akron, OH 34890
(216)555-5712 • Fax (216)555-3009

July 17, 20—

Alyson Chambers
468 Summers Street, Apt. 410
Edwardsville, IL 64475-3019

**WOK HEATING ELEMENT**

**1** Wok cooking offers health-conscious people delicious meals with very low fat content. This is possible because the heat is spread evenly throughout the cooking surface. The key to even cooking temperatures is the heating element.

**2** When your letter and package arrived, they were delivered to our repair division. Upon opening the element's casing, the technician discovered that the parts inside were wet—a clear sign that the element had been placed in water or that water had been spilled on it. The owner's manual for the wok **3** indicates that the heating element should be cleaned by wiping it with a damp cloth. Exposing the element to water would cause the unit to fail. The warranty would be void.

**4** To restore your wok to working condition, the heating element must be replaced. New elements are available for $29.95; reconditioned elements are available for $19.95. A new element would have the same one-year warranty as the original element. The warranty on reconditioned units is in effect for just three months.

**5** To order either a new or a reconditioned element, phone 1-800-555-6060. Within ten days after placing your order, you'll again be "woking" your way to good health.

Vicki Haugen
Customer Service Representative

**Figure 5-2**
Adjustment Refusal

## SUBJECT LINES

Assume you are the claimant in the situation leading to Figure 5-2. Would you react positively or negatively to a message that began with each of the following subject lines? Why?

DEFECTIVE HEATING ELEMENT

WET HEATING ELEMENT

YOUR REQUEST FOR REPAIR

REPLACEMENT OF HEATING ELEMENT

One final comment about refusal messages: Be sure they are timely. Delays in responding to requests or claims could make readers angry and less willing to accept bad news.

*Refusals must be timely.*

## Unexpected Bad News

This type of bad news message deserves special attention. It, more than any other type of bad news message, will be received with disappointment or anger. The reason for these reactions is simple—the readers aren't expecting any message, let alone bad news. Layoffs, terminations, reductions in benefits, increases in price, or reductions in service are all unexpected bad news.

These messages, like other bad news messages, begin with a buffer. Because the receiver isn't aware of the topic of the message, the buffer

*Receiver analysis is especially important in unexpected bad news situations.*

must outline it clearly. The buffer in unexpected bad news messages may, therefore, be longer than the buffer in request refusal or adjustment refusal messages.

After providing a clear, complete explanation of the situation, the writer gives the bad news. While implied bad news is less emphatic, expressed bad news may be needed for clarity.

Counterproposals show a writer's empathy for a receiver's situation.

The counterproposal/resale section is critical in an unexpected bad news message. Any alternative solution or offer of assistance will show interest in readers and help them to accept the bad news. The message should close with a positive, optimistic statement.

Assume that an income tax preparation service wishes to announce that its rates will be increased by an unusually large amount. The service recently replaced its aging computer system and upgraded its tax software. The costs will be passed to customers. Figure 5-3 shows how the tax service approached this unexpected bad news message.

Because the writer of this bad news message stresses reader benefit from the start of the letter, the buffer is not only short but also positive. It clearly identifies the topic, and it provides a good transition to the explanation.

The explanation, like the buffer, is positive. It stresses reader benefit and minimizes the bad news. Prices are listed in an enclosure rather than in the letter because cost is based on the complexity of the return. Resale begins at the end of the second paragraph and continues through the close.

The address is missing and the salutation is incomplete because the writer wants to personalize the form message for each client.

# THE DIRECT APPROACH

Rules, it has been said, are meant to be broken, and that is the case with the approach to writing bad news messages. Although an indirect approach is used in *almost* all cases involving bad news, a direct approach may be best in special cases.

Occasionally, bad news should be conveyed directly.

Use the direct approach if previous experience with a receiver suggests that the indirect approach will be unsuccessful. Be direct when writing indirectly could be perceived as being deceptive. These situations could include labor-management negotiations and product recalls.

Use the direct plan when confirming information that has already been presented orally.

The direct approach is also appropriate when the written message confirms negative news previously conveyed orally. This oral/written communication blend works well when the bad news has considerable emotional impact. For example, a supervisor who must terminate an employee would initially convey the news in a one-to-one meeting and then follow-up with a written confirmation. Similarly, if a company had a long-standing relationship with one supplier and then decided to award a contract to another, the news would probably be conveyed face-to-face or by telephone first. This technique shows personal and organizational sensitivity.

Thompson's Tax Service
112B Kenwood Mall Annex
Pierre, SD 58613
(605) 555-0775

January 2, 20—

Dear :

1 Accurate tax preparation at reasonable rates. That's what you want; that's what we provide.

2 This year, QUICK can be added to the list of words describing our tax service. The powerful computer system and new tax software we've installed will help us to get your completed return to you within five days after we receive your records. That's a full week faster than in previous years—an advantage sure to offset the new, higher rates (see enclosed listing). Remember, speedier processing

3 means an earlier refund or more time to plan how to pay what you owe.

4 The computer has been installed and the tax preparers have been trained. All that's missing is you! Call today to schedule your appointment for FAST, accurate tax preparation.

Martha Thompson
Manager

Enclosure

## Annotations

1. Buffer
2. Explanation
3. Bad News
   Resale
4. Positive Close

**Figure 5-3**
Unexpected Bad News Message

> **"The degree of one's emotion varies inversely with one's knowledge of the facts—the less you know, the hotter you get."**
>
> —Bertrand Russell

**Think twice before sending bad news by e-mail.**

## WORKPLACE CONNECTIONS

If you choose to send bad news by e-mail, read the message several times to ensure style, accuracy, and tone.

# PROPER USE OF TECHNOLOGY

Technology has had a tremendous effect on the way written communication is created and transmitted. When it comes to bad news messages, though, writers should carefully consider the role technology can and should play. Clearly, e-mail represents an efficient way to respond to questions or complaints. If those messages were sent by e-mail, it is appropriate to respond to them electronically, using the indirect or direct approach as dictated by receiver and situation analysis. When the bad news is unexpected or has substantial emotional impact, traditional distribution methods should be used; e-mail is too informal and direct.

# CHAPTER SUMMARY

◆ Bad news business messages include request refusals, adjustment refusals, and unexpected bad news.

◆ The indirect approach is typically used when conveying bad news.

◆ The indirect approach to conveying bad news has five sections:

1. *Buffer.* An opening that is on the topic of the message but does not reveal the bad news.

2. *Explanation.* Convincing reasons that lead the reader to accept the negative news.

3. *Bad News.* An implied or expressed statement given minimal emphasis in the message.

4. *Counterproposal/Resale.* Additional reasons, alternative solutions, or comments designed to maintain or rebuild goodwill between the sender and receiver.

5. *Closing.* A positive statement that relates to the topic without referencing the bad news.

◆ The direct approach may be used in special circumstances, as dictated by receiver and situation analysis.

◆ E-mail can deliver some bad news messages, but bad news that is sensitive or important should be sent by letter or conveyed orally.

words@work Go to the Writing Tab; access and read the lesson on Business Letters. Complete the appropriate *words@work* exercises.

# CHAPTER 5 APPLICATIONS

**SECTION I** ***Work-related Messages.*** The following exercises require you to apply the indirect approach. Read the directions carefully. Unless specified in the text or by your instructor, you may choose the memo/letter style you prefer (refer to Appendix A). Be sure to apply the 4Cs of communication covered in Chapter 3, and remember to proofread for both content and mechanics.

## Request Refusals

1. You have been invited to join the local chapter of Alpha Beta Gamma (ABG), a group for business professionals. Each chapter of the group has a membership limit of just 25; the last time the local chapter accepted a member was 1993. According to the invitation, signed by Membership Chair E. Jacob Zenk, the initiation ceremony—which new members *must* attend—is scheduled for February 20. As sales manager for Falls Industries, you travel frequently. In fact, you will be out of town from February 19 through 22, meeting with an important client.

   - Assume that you have decided to decline the invitation to join Alpha Beta Gamma.

       a. Who will read your message?


       b. Will you use a letter, memo, or other format (specify)?


       c. What idea will you use in the buffer?


       d. What details will you furnish as part of your explanation?


       e. Will you imply or express the bad news?


       f. Will you use a counterproposal, provide resale information, or offer additional reasons?


       g. What will be the basis of your counterproposal/resale/reason section?

h. What positive item can you use as a closing?

i. Are enclosures needed? If so, what?

j. Using the notes you made in items a–i above, write the message.

2. Refer to the case in exercise 1. Assume the role of president of the local chapter of Alpha Beta Gamma. J. P. Riche, a prospective member, has asked that initiation ceremony requirements be modified to allow her to join ABG at the March 20 meeting. Much as you wish you could do so, you can't. The requirement is one set by the national board, not the local board. Prepare a message that refuses the request.

3. You work for Will Macor, manager of the Accounting Department at Billings Manufacturing. Your company pays tuition and fees for employees who take classes related to their jobs. When a worker wants to enroll for a class, he/she submits a written request to his/her supervisor. After completing an approved class, the worker submits his/her grade report and proof of expenses. Today (August 23) is the first day of Will's five-week vacation. Although Will won't be in today, he has left some work for you to complete. Among the items he's left for you are the following memo and draft response. Will's note says "Finish this refusal for me; sign my name." Do as Will asks.

*Incoming Memo:*

    *TO:       Will Macor, Manager*

    *FROM:   Pamela Fox, Account Clerk*

    *DATE:   August 20, 20—*

    *SUBJECT:  COURSE ENROLLMENT*

*Will, may I have your permission to enroll for the following class at Cambridge Community College:*

COMM 101 Mass Media

*Mass media is a topic that's always interested me, and I'd like to learn more about it in this 3-credit class. Fall term begins September 11; I'll need your approval by September 4 to enable me to register.*

- - - - - - - - - - - - - - - - - - - - - - - - - - - - - - - - - - - - - - - - - - - -

*Draft Memo:*

    TO:       Pamela Fox, Account Clerk

    FROM:   Will Macor, Manager

    DATE:   August 23, 20—

    SUBJECT:

Pam, it's good to see that you're interested in taking classes at Cambridge Community College. CCC is a fine school with many classes that can benefit Billings' employees.

In order to promote professional growth and assure that workers are aware of innovations in their fields, Billings pays tuition and fees for workers who enroll for courses directly related to their work.

4. You are the program coordinator for Professional Development, Inc. (PDI). Your company hires well-known authors and speakers to conduct seminars on topics of interest to business professionals. In order to meet expenses, you must enroll 10 people in each seminar. The maximum number of participants in each seminar is 25. The seminar leaders appreciate the small class size, and smaller numbers make it easy for you to locate sites for the sessions. Brochures are prepared and distributed to people throughout the nation. Each brochure describes a particular seminar and its dates and locations. A registration form is part of the brochure. Only mail registrations are accepted because the full fee must be submitted with the form. One seminar currently being offered by PDI is "Improving Your Written Communication Skills." Cities, sites, dates, and current enrollments for the seminar are:

| | | | |
|---|---|---|---|
| Albuquerque, New Mexico | Old Town Center | May 27 | 7 |
| Chicago, Illinois | Executive Hotel | May 23 | 21 |
| Dallas, Texas | Houston House | May 25 | 25 |
| Fort Worth, Texas | Rio Grande Suites | May 26 | 18 |
| St. Louis, Missouri | Arch Plaza | May 24 | 20 |

Today is May 15, the closing date for the writing seminar. You receive three reservations for the Dallas seminar.

a. Prepare a form letter to be sent to the people who registered for the Albuquerque seminar telling them it has been canceled.

b. Prepare a form letter to be sent to each of the three people whose registrations were received after the Dallas seminar was filled. Pay special attention to the counterproposal section; use it to persuade the readers to attend the seminar in Fort Worth.

5. Your office needs a new photocopier. Several weeks ago, you asked local office equipment dealers to submit bids. You've reviewed the bids, read the literature that accompanied them, and seen demonstrations of the various models. You've decided the CopyMaster 302 is the model for you. Write the remaining bidders telling them you'll be purchasing your copier from another vendor.

6. Helena O'Brien teaches aerobics classes. She's written to your company, Sims Publications, requesting 250 reprints of "Dance for Health." She wants to give the reprints to people who enroll in her classes. The article appeared on pages 113–118 of the June 1996 issue of *Healthy Heart*. Rather than send so many copies of the article to one person, you will send her one copy and give her permission to reprint as many copies as she needs for her students. Your message should include the reprint statement you want to appear on the copies. [Hint: Check a reference manual for ideas on how to write the credit line.]

7. Employees of your company may participate in any of four different health plans. Employees are free to move from one plan to another as their needs change, but shifts between plans may occur only once each calendar year. Today (August 17) you, the employee benefits clerk, receive a request from Virginia Marthaller to change from Plan A to Plan B. A check of Virginia's file reveals that she switched to Plan A on June 15. Prepare an appropriate message to this auditing department worker.

8. As corporate communications director for a paper products company, you often receive requests to donate products (e.g., facial tissue, bath tissue) to charitable organizations. Your organization has a philosophy that endorses corporate giving to agencies that operate in the communities where you have offices and factories. Prepare a form letter that could be sent to organizations that do not meet your giving criteria.

9. When you checked your e-mail this morning, you found a message from your supervisor asking whether it will be possible for you to finish a staffing report a week earlier than the original due date because he will be out of town on business and would like to review the report while away. Normally, you organize your projects to enable you to complete them with days to spare. This time, though, your schedule has no flexibility. Your assistant resigned, the database you needed had to be updated before you could use it, and you will be taking at least three days of sick leave next week because of minor surgery that was scheduled months ago. Prepare an appropriate response.

# Adjustment Refusals

10. You work in the customer service department of a mail order company that sells return address labels. Today you receive the following letter:

   To Whom It May Concern:

   Enclosed are the labels I ordered from you last month. My fiancé and I decided not to get married, so the labels are inaccurate. Please send me a $4.65 refund.

   Brenda Davis

   901 5th Avenue South, Apt. 6

   Santa Fe, NM 88046

   You will, of course, refuse Brenda's request for a refund.

11. You manage an advertising business that provides custom-made novelty products. Last month, The George Company ordered 1,500 insulated sip cups from you. Each mug was to show the company name, logo, and motto. Today, you received a fax from Petri George, a vice president at the company. He's irate because the cups say "The Gorge Company." He wants you to replace the cups, deliver them at your expense, and refund 50 percent of the purchase price. You try to avoid content errors by sending customers a proof (draft illustration) before production begins. You've examined your records and see that this text, including the error, was approved by someone with the initials *plg*. Deny the claim.

12. The gallery you manage sells a variety of artwork, including framed and unframed paintings and prints. The walls of your shop are adorned with attractively framed items. Each has a small card posted on or near it showing the title of the work, the name of the artist, and the "framed" and "unframed" price. Last week, Kwan Chee purchased a framed print of Arden Harvey's *Raging River* as a gift for a colleague who was retiring. Kwan was in a hurry the day he made the selection. After removing it from the wall and setting it on the counter, he asked you to bill him and said someone would stop for the package two days later. Everything seemed to go as planned until today, two weeks after Kwan's visit to your shop. In the mail you find a letter from a very angry Kwan, who insists you overcharged him. Although he makes reference to the framed print, he quotes the price of the unframed work. Handle his claim.

13. Marlow Gunderson has written to you expressing dissatisfaction with your homemade salsa, Hot Shot. The product, he asserts, is "hotter than the desert sun in August." He doesn't think that the symbol you use to indicate the warmth of the salsa (red flames; 1 = mild; 5 = extreme) is effective. He goes on to suggest a new symbol and wording that, frankly, isn't appropriate for a label; he's enclosed a bill for $300, which he says represents the cost of his services. Respond to his claim.

14. You work as a customer service agent for a regional airline. Louis Rodrigo has requested a $140 refund on the unused portion of a round-trip ticket, which he enclosed with his letter. He says he arrived at the airport 30 minutes prior to the flight. After making his way to the front of a long line, he learned the departure time had been changed and he had missed his flight. There were no other flights that day, so he spent the night at a hotel and returned on another airline. He's asking for $400 to cover those costs. The ticket was purchased during a promotion that offered travelers a low price in return for 30-day advance booking and a minimum 5-day stay that included a Saturday night. All ads and the ticket receipt clearly indicated "No Refunds." Mr. Harvey is correct in saying that the flight time was changed; however, new itineraries were mailed to those affected by the change. Every itinerary also bears a bright orange sticker saying, "To ensure adequate time for check-in and boarding, please arrive at the airport at least 60 minutes prior to the scheduled departure time." Respond to the claim.

## Unexpected Bad News

15. You are a programmer for Destinations Unlimited, a travel agency specializing in overseas tours. One of the tours your firm is currently offering is a 7-day trip to London, England. Included in the $2,150 fee are airfare, hotel accommodations, breakfast each day, a bus tour of the city, two theater performances, and a day trip to Windsor Castle. A $500 nonrefundable deposit is required when reservations are made. Your clients pay you in U.S. money, but you must pay your London expenses in British currency, called pounds. The value of the U.S. dollar against the British pound changes daily. Unfortunately, the value of the dollar has fallen over the past few months. In fact, the fee necessary to cover expenses must be increased to $2,475. The people who signed up for the tour knew that the $2,150 fee was subject to change, but you aren't sure how they will react to a $325 increase. Your task is to tell them.

16. The bank at which you work offers many services to its clients, including safety deposit boxes. The boxes are available in four sizes. Bank patrons lease their boxes on a year-to-year basis. An annual fee is charged; bills are sent one month before the leases expire. The bank has decided to raise the box fee. The sizes, current fees, and new fees are:

| | | |
|---|---|---|
| 2" × 5" box | $10.00 | $12.50 |
| 4" × 6" box | $12.50 | $15.00 |
| 6" × 10" box | $18.00 | $22.00 |
| 8" × 12" box | $25.00 | $30.00 |

Prepare a form message that can be sent to each person whose lease is about to expire notifying him/her about the rate increase.

17. For the past month, the employees of your firm have donated money to help Bobby Burns. Bobby, the 8-month-old son of maintenance worker Harry Burns, needed a kidney transplant. Containers were placed in several locations throughout the building; people were encouraged to make cash deposits. The drive was very successful; $1,873 has been donated. This morning you learn Bobby died yesterday. Prepare a memo to the staff telling them the bad news. Be sure to indicate what will be done with the money that has been collected.

18. With three of your classmates, assume the role of your company's Employee Advisory Board. Among the Board's responsibilities is evaluating suggestions submitted by staff members. Today, you review a memo from Ben Whitby, Samantha Woodward, and Heather Duff. The three suggest that, because casual day has been so successful, the company should—during June, July, and August only—have daily themes. Specifically, they propose the following:

- Mad Hatter Monday; employees wear hats.

- Teen Time Tuesdays; workers dress as they did when they were teenagers.

- Wild Wig Wednesdays; employees wear wigs or unique hair styles.

- T-Shirt Thursdays; workers wear t-shirts and shorts.

- Gone Fishin' Fridays, employees dress as though they are at a lake or on a fishing trip.

These sound like fun, but at your work site more than 30 percent of the workforce has daily face-to-face contact with the public. You've had casual Fridays for about a year, and you've noticed that the clothing has deteriorated from business casual to home casual. Rumor has it that Human Resources will soon issue guidelines to be followed for casual Friday attire. Respond to the group's suggestion. As part of your work, do an Internet search and read articles related to other organizations' experiences with casual days or similar events.

19. You are a sales associate with Bayfield Furniture. Three months ago, you worked with Sheila and Roberto Alm to select living room and dining room furniture for their new home. The Alm's were delighted when their dining room furniture arrived a week ahead of the projected delivery date. The news you have for them today, however, won't please them. The company that manufactures the sofa, love seat, and chairs the Alm's ordered just notified you that the fabric they chose is out of stock. The Alm's have two options, neither of which will please them. (1) They may wait for the fabric of their choice; their furniture will be delivered in 10–12 weeks. (2) They may select an in-stock fabric, and their furniture will be delivered in 4–6 weeks. Write to your customers.

20. For the past 8 years, Kuntz Paper Company has sponsored a picnic for its workers and their families or guests. The all-day event was held at a local park. Food and beverages were provided. There were games for adults and children; prizes were awarded. The past year has been a difficult one for Kuntz. A fire severely damaged one of the warehouses. Customers went elsewhere for their products; revenues fell. Also, the actual cost of installing a new pollution control system far exceeded the estimate. Therefore, this year's company picnic will be replaced with an "employees only" ice cream social. Notify the employees of the change.

21. As business manager for *Golden Glow Senior Residence*, you face the task of telling residents that the cost of relocating from one apartment to another will rise from $40 to $400. Each time an apartment becomes vacant, it is thoroughly cleaned. The new rate more nearly matches the actual time/materials cost of this process. Your residents, most of whom are on fixed incomes, won't like this news. Senior citizen housing is in short supply. Because your facility has offered vacant units to tenants before applicants, many people moved into their current apartments with the intent of moving to apartments with more space or a better view.

22. You've just returned from a meeting chaired by your friend and colleague, Fred Selby, and find the following e-mail from him:

    Whew! That was a ruf mtg, but all-in-all, I think it went well, don't u?

Truthfully, you don't think the meeting went well at all. Fred was extremely disorganized and tried to dominate the meeting. At one point, two of the participants started to argue with one another, and Fred didn't intervene. Closure was reached on only one of the six items discussed, and the meeting went 30 minutes beyond its announced ending time. The group is scheduled to meet again in two weeks, but no one is sure who is to do what between now and then.

When you respond to Fred's message, provide information and resources to assist him in improving his meeting leadership skills. The following URLs are a place to start, but don't restrict yourself to information contained in them:

> *http://www.advantagemgmt.com/resource/meetings2.html*

> *http://www.srg.co.uk/meetings.html*

In addition, recommend two or three print resources Fred might review. A search of the following Internet bookstores may help:

> *http://www.amazon.com*

> *http://www.borders.com*

> *http://bn.com*

23. You work in the Administrative Services Department for the City of Smithville. One of your tasks is scheduling use of city vehicles. During the past month you have received calls and letters from citizens of Smithville complaining that they have seen city cars parked at local grocery stores, malls, and entertainment facilities. Prepare a memo reminding workers that city cars are to be used only for city business.

24. While reviewing last month's long distance phone bill, you noticed that Paige Hilsen had made seven long-distance calls after business hours. (The computerized billing report identifies callers by code.) You've spoken to Paige, and she's admitted the calls were personal, a violation of company policy. She's agreed to pay for the calls. You won't discipline Paige, but you do want an official record of the incident and remedy. Prepare a memo that accomplishes your goal; show that a copy will be placed in Paige's personnel file.

25. Deborah Winston, your supervisor and manager of the accounting department, has asked you to prepare a memo telling workers that receipts will now be required for reimbursement of all business-related expenses. Currently, only expenses in excess of $50 require receipts.

SECTION II  *Personal Business Messages.* The following exercises relate to some aspect of using the indirect approach in writing situations you might face in your personal life. Read the directions carefully. Select a letter style appropriate for a personal business message—one that includes your return address (refer to Appendix A). Be sure to follow the 4Cs of communication presented in Chapter 3. Plan before writing, and proofread for both content and mechanics.

26. You have been invited to serve on the planning committee for your high school reunion, but have decided to decline. Write to Barb Zelnick telling her the bad news.

27. You belong to the student chapter of a professional organization. The local group that sponsors your chapter selected you to be this year's recipient of its "Rising Star" award. You were the organization's guest at its dinner meeting last night, at which time they presented you with a plaque and a $100 check. Your name is spelled correctly on the check, but not on the plaque. You didn't want to destroy the mood or embarrass anyone at the dinner, so you decided to wait until today to write to Jason Kilpatrick, the president, to tell him the bad news.

28. You volunteer at a local homeless shelter and soup kitchen on weekends. You enjoy working with the shelter's clients but, because you have considerable experience with computers, the coordinator asked you to devote the majority of your volunteer hours to the business side of the operation. When you got to the office today, you found a note from the coordinator asking you to install two software programs. You quickly noticed that the programs are not licensed. Although you know the shelter has a small operating budget, you object to installing pirated software. Convey the bad news to Olivia Newfeld.

29. You have been asked by the president of your school to serve as its representative to the local United Way's planning committee. This is quite an honor, and something that would look good on your resume. Also, you believe in contributing not only money but also time to charitable organizations. If you accept the responsibility, you would be expected to attend bi-weekly meetings—some midday, others evening—throughout July and August, participate in the kick-off barbeque, and coordinate all fundraising efforts at your school. Decline.

30. Your good friend Terry Brennan attends school in another city. While she was home for a break several months ago, you and Terry had lunch. You chatted about lots of things, including your mutual love of books. During the conversation, Terry mentioned a mystery novel she'd just finished and thought you would enjoy reading. After she returned to school, she mailed it to you. The book was so good you read it from cover to cover and then passed it along to your cousin, Marv. Today you receive an e-mail from Terry asking you to mail the book to her because she wants to give it back to the person from whom she had borrowed it. This is the first you knew that the book wasn't Terry's or that you weren't free to share it with someone else. Unfortunately, Marv can't find the book. Respond to Terry's request.

# WRITING PERSUASIVE MESSAGES

A hypnotist slowly waves a watch or other object before a subject's eyes and says "You are getting sleepy, very sleepy." Once the subject is relaxed, the hypnotist tells the subject to do things that otherwise would not be acceptable: walk like a duck, moo like a cow, tango without a partner, or laugh when a particular word is spoken. The techniques used in business messages are far less dramatic, but the desired result is the same. The sender wants to persuade the receiver to do something he or she may not want to do.

## INDIRECT APPROACH

Persuasion is a little bit science, a little bit art. The science stems from techniques that have been developed through experience and experimentation. The art relates to the ability of people to use the techniques effectively.

Persuasive messages are most often associated with sales, but many other business situations also require persuasion. Requests, claims, debt collections, and proposals all require persuasion. In fact, anytime someone wants cooperation, money, information, support, or time from someone who is likely to resist, persuasion is required.

If persuaders were allowed to choose, most would prefer to deliver their messages orally, face-to-face. In this setting, the persuader can gauge the receiver's reaction and adjust the message based on what is heard or observed. In addition, an in-person request is harder to refuse than a written one or one delivered by telephone. Time, distance, and cost make it impractical or impossible for all persuasive messages to be delivered in person, so communicators must write persuasive messages. Written messages are more persuasive when they use the indirect approach.

The indirect approach uses *attention, interest, desire,* and *action* (AIDA) to create persuasive messages. The parts are presented in sequence, but the result doesn't have to be a four-paragraph message. The topic, reader, and situation will influence the length of the interest and desire sections.

### LEARNING OBJECTIVES

- Learn to write persuasive messages using the indirect approach.
- Use *attention, interest, desire,* and *action* (AIDA) to make the indirect approach work.
- Write persuasive sales messages, requests, claims, and collection letters.
- Compose effective business proposals.

*Use the indirect approach for persuasive messages.*

*Persuasive messages use the AIDA plan.*

# Attention

A persuasive message begins with an attention-getting opening. The opening should involve readers by being of interest to them. Some attention-getting message openers are:

*Question*        Would you like to vacation in the Caribbean?

*Statement*       Just 30 minutes of your time could save a life.

*Compliment*      Thanks to you and other volunteers, last year's scholarship drive was a success.

*Bargain/Gift*    Enjoy the convenience of a cellular phone without roaming charges.

*Fact*            ABC's energy costs have risen 15 percent in the past year.

*Problem*         Delivery delays cost Bixby's more than $1,000 a week.

*Story*           It wasn't easy for Martha after Allen died. By working two jobs, she was able to earn enough money to provide her three young children with simple, nutritious meals and a clean place to live.

# Interest

After getting the receiver's attention, build interest by keeping the reader focused on the topic. Describe the product, service, or idea and show how the reader will benefit from it. Stress the feature or concept that you believe will have the greatest influence on the receiver. One or more of the following appeals usually work:

| | |
|---|---|
| Approval | Money |
| Beauty | Pleasure |
| Comfort | Prestige |
| Convenience | Pride |
| Efficiency | Recognition |
| Enjoyment | Respect |
| Fame | Safety |
| Friendship | Security |
| Good Health | Success |
| Intelligence | Time |
| Love | Wealth |

*Chapter 6: Writing Persuasive Messages*

## ATTENTION AND INTEREST

For each product, service, or idea in the following list, identify at least two appeals that could be used to show reader benefit. Consider appeals in addition to those listed earlier in this section.

| Idea, Product, or Service | Reader | Appeals |
|---|---|---|
| carpet cleaning | homeowner | _____ |
| changing location of supply cabinet | office supervisor | _____ |
| computer | insurance agent | _____ |
| stapler | office worker | _____ |
| tax preparation | sales associate | _____ |

Select one of the items above and write an attention-getting opening for the message:

Suddenly, Sam realizes he's going to have to work harder at identifying reader benefits.

After generating interest in the topic, the writer works to make the receiver *want* the benefits that have been described; the writer creates desire.

## Desire

As the writer moves from interest to desire, the focus of the message shifts from an emotional appeal to a logical one. The shift should be so smooth and natural that it is difficult to tell where the interest section ends and the desire section begins. Facts, figures, guarantees, samples, or testimonials are used to build the receiver's desire to act. In order to keep the desire section to a reasonable length, writers often include brochures, reports, or other descriptive items with their messages. Savvy writers recognize that such enclosures enhance the desire section but do not replace it. They refer to the enclosures only after developing one or more strong selling points.

In addition to documenting the value of the product, service, or idea, the writer uses the desire section to overcome reader objections. One of the most common objections readers have is cost. Price can't be overlooked, but it can be minimized. Expressing the total cost of a product or service in daily, weekly, or monthly charges makes the price seem affordable. Rather than saying a new air conditioner will cost $750, tell the reader that cool comfort is available for less than $2.25 a day. Indicate how long it will take for the product/service to pay for itself. Speak about the number of minutes that can be saved, how much productivity can be increased, or how many errors will be eliminated by using the product or service.

Throughout the interest and desire sections, the writer works to make the reader want to take advantage of the product, service, or idea. Some writers are tempted to stretch the truth or make wild statements about benefits. Exaggerations make the reader lose interest in the message and think poorly of the writer. If the message is external, the image of the business can be tarnished. If the message is internal, the credibility of the writer can be questioned. The problem, however, doesn't end there. Making incomplete or false statements is unethical and can be illegal. Honesty is the best policy.

When readers have finished reading the desire section, they should ask, "What do I do next?" The answer is provided in the *action* section.

## Action

In this section, the writer clearly, concisely, and confidently shows what the reader must do to get the benefits described in the interest section. The writer lists phone numbers; encloses reply cards or postage-paid, self-addressed envelopes; or expresses willingness to discuss the topic. Prompt action is encouraged by offering discounts, offering to bill the reader at a later date, or setting a deadline by which action must be taken. Message unity is achieved by referring once again to the benefits the reader will receive. Goodwill is achieved by maintaining a courteous tone.

## DESIRE AND ACTION

Last year your company paid $500 to rent an 8′ × 10′ display space at a business products show. You are proposing that: (1) Your company participate in the show again, and (2) you double the size of your display space. The larger display area will cost $1,250.

What facts/figures could you present to convince your supervisor to display at the show this year?

Your annual advertising budget is $7,500. How can you overcome your supervisor's objection to spending 1/6 of your annual budget on one event?

Do you think setting a date by which your supervisor should respond is "pushy"? Why or why not?

# TYPES OF PERSUASIVE MESSAGES

AIDA can be used in various business messages including sales messages, requests, claims, debt collections, and proposals.

# Sales Messages

Sales messages are different from other persuasive messages in the following ways:

**LENGTH.** Sales messages routinely exceed one page. Most recipients don't read the entire message. The writers hope, however, that something in the mass of text will pique readers' interest enough to make them buy the product or service.

**USE OF ENCLOSURES.** Sales messages frequently include photos, brochures, coupons, samples, and return envelopes.

**UNCONVENTIONAL GRAMMAR/PUNCTUATION.** Sentence fragments, exclamation points, and ellipsis points are used to hold interest and achieve a conversational style. These techniques are improper in other business messages.

**VISUAL DEVICES.** Colored paper, colored ink, unusual stationery sizes, type style/size variations, and indented text are some of the visual devices that can be used to enhance sales messages and get reader attention.

*Getting receivers to read a sales message requires special effort.*

To minimize mailing costs, sales messages are often sent via third-class bulk mail. The rapidly increasing volume of third-class mail has prompted writers to find other ways to make their messages stand out. Some try to attract readers' attention by making the envelope unique. A black envelope with white printing is distinctive. A bright orange label with FREE GIFT ENCLOSED printed on it attracts attention and encourages the reader to look inside. Captions such as *Important, Limited Time Offer*, and *You're a Winner* can motivate receivers to read the message.

*Some sales messages are creative; others are traditional.*

Some writers believe readers are immune to these techniques and throw away third-class mail without opening it. Therefore, writers try to make their third-class mail look like first-class mail. Return addresses are subtle rather than bold. Individually prepared envelopes replace those with labels. Stamps are used in place of metered mail. Stationery will be white, tan, or grey; and both the return and mailing addresses will be color-coordinated with the stationery.

Many of the techniques described here have become common in Internet sales messages. The presentation will offer many things on the same page with headlines to attract attention. Instead of enclosures, links to other pages are provided. Color and type choices are used to draw the reader's eye. In addition, the Internet offers the opportunity to use animation and sound to attract attention. Log onto the Internet and check your mail for the next week, and you will find examples of these sales techniques.

# Requests

The key to writing an effective persuasive request is showing how the request benefits the reader. It is also important to include enough details to enable the reader to give the request full consideration. Figure 6-1 shows a letter asking a business leader to serve on the committee to plan the city's Fourth of July celebration.

*Requests must show reader benefit and provide complete details.*

**Madison Chamber of Commerce**
56 James Street
Madison, WI 53389
(608) 555-3521

October 12, 20—

Mr. Peter Hulliman
345 James Road
Madison, WI 54486

Dear Mr. Hulliman:

**1** What's your favorite Independence Day memory, Mr. Hulliman? Perhaps you remember marching in the parade. Maybe you recall eating popcorn, hot dogs, and cotton candy at the fairgrounds. Possibly you picture yourself watching the fireworks at Camp Randall Stadium.

**2** Memories like these don't just happen—they are made. Friends and family make them happen. You can make them happen by working "behind the scenes" to plan events that will be remembered by people of all ages.

**3** A five-member planning group meets once a month October through June. The two-hour meetings are held at City Hall; dates and times are set to fit members' schedules. Each member of the planning group heads a subcommittee of community volunteers. The various subcommittees work independently to accomplish their tasks. In addition to receiving a Chamber of Commerce "Committed Citizen" certificate of participation, each planning committee member enjoys the privilege of riding on the Chamber's float in the Independence Day parade.

**4** Gretta McClaren, president of McClaren and Associates, will chair the planning committee. Please join her and other civic-minded business professionals in making the next Fourth of July Celebration a memorable one. To indicate your willingness to serve on the planning committee, simply complete and return the enclosed postcard by October 31.

Sincerely,

Jason Ritzer, President

Enclosure

## Annotations

**1.** Gains attention by asking a personalized question

**2.** Builds interest by continuing memory theme

**3.** Creates desire by minimizing time commitment

**4.** Ends by making action easy; relates again to memory theme

**Figure 6-1**
Persuasive Request

Notice how the opening is personalized by using the name of the receiver. The theme, a memorable holiday, is introduced in the opening paragraph, developed in paragraph two, and referred to again in the close. Since the reader is a busy business professional, one objection he might have to the request is the time involved if he accepts. The writer overcomes this objection by outlining the frequency and length of the meetings. Reader benefits are also identified.

Finally, the reader is told how to respond. Action is made easy by enclosing a reply card. Setting a deadline helps get quick action.

## Claims

Claims may be either routine or persuasive. The difference is the anticipated reaction of the reader. If you order merchandise and it arrives in damaged condition, you expect the seller to replace it; your claim will be direct. If, however, the merchandise arrives in good condition but malfunctions after its warranty expires, you should anticipate that the manufacturer or seller will resist making repairs without charge; your request will have to be persuasive.

Unlike routine claims, which begin with a direct statement of the problem, persuasive claims begin with one or more statements to set the context of the message. If there is some positive aspect of the situation, the opening paragraph might mention it.

In the interest section of a persuasive claim, the writer outlines the events that led to writing the message. Specific dates are helpful, but not essential. Negative words may be needed to clarify the dissatisfaction. Explaining what inconvenience has been experienced increases the seller's desire to remedy the situation.

The writer provides the details then requests an adjustment. The requested adjustment must be reasonable; it must be stated clearly. Include the date by which the receiver should respond or take action. If the writer asks the reader to telephone, include the number and a good time to make contact.

Claims should be presented calmly, clearly, and completely to have the best chance of succeeding. Messages that have an angry tone or threaten the reader are not persuasive.

Figure 6-2 shows a claim letter that states the purpose of the message and gives the positive aspects of the situation early in the message. As the message is developed, the writer gives specific details of the claim and requests definite action. A time frame for response is included, and phone numbers are provided to make action easy.

## Collection Messages

Whenever a business loans money or provides services or goods on credit, there is a chance that customers will not pay their bills on time. Generally, one or more of the following conditions has prompted customers to delay their payments:

*If possible, begin a persuasive claim by commenting on any positive aspect of the situation.*

*Explain events clearly; use negative words if necessary.*

*Request a reasonable adjustment; set a date for action.*

*Avoid showing anger or making threats.*

March 21, 20—

Mr. Steve Goodhue
Goodhue's Remodeling
2356 Stebner Road
Marquette, MI 51220

Dear Steve:

**1** Last fall your workers installed 17 new windows in my home. We chose to replace our Carson and Carson windows with others by the same manufacturer because you said no structural modifications would be required.

**2** The work was completed on schedule, and we were able to observe the ghosts and goblins of Halloween through clear panes of glass. By Thanksgiving the wood had been stained, and we were able to rehang our window coverings. Everything seemed perfect . . . until last week.

**3** When I opened the sheer draperies so that I might wash the windows, I noticed stains beside and beneath the right panel of the six-window set in the living room. In addition, that window had a vapor leak. The stains appear to have been caused by moisture from melting snow seeping through the window insulation; the vapor leak may be the result of a manufacturing defect.

**4** Photos showing the extent of the damage are enclosed. Neither the stains nor the vapor leak were present when the draperies were rehung in November. Replacement of the window with the leak is covered by the 10-year warranty Carson and Carson issued when we bought the windows. Repair of damage to the vapor wall of my home, however, is your responsibility. Please phone me within the next two weeks to discuss the best time for you to replace the window and the insulation, repair the drywall, and repaint the wall. I may be reached at 555-0295 during the day or at 555-8917 in the evening.

Sincerely,

Henry Bianchet
2748 Woodward Lane
Marquette, MI 51222

Enclosures

**1.** Opening sets context for claim.

**2.** Positive statements about work.

**3.** Problem described.

**4.** Specific action is requested; phone numbers are given.

**Figure 6-2**
Persuasive Claim

- They have simply overlooked the billing statement.
- They don't have enough money to pay the bill.
- They are dissatisfied with the service or the merchandise.
- They seldom pay on time; late or missed payments are a habit.

Regardless of the cause of the problem, businesses must try to collect. If customers don't pay, the business may be unable to meet its obligations to employees and creditors. Its profits could decline.

*Collection messages are persuasive messages.*

As important as it is to collect what it is due, business professionals realize they are dealing with people. They recognize and respect the role pride plays in collection situations. Therefore, they approach collection messages in three stages: reminder, appeal, and warning.

**REMINDER.** In the reminder stage, writers assume that readers want to pay but have simply overlooked the bill. Reminders are often light-hearted. Some commonly used tactics include a computer-generated message printed on a copy of the statement, a bright sticker on a copy of the bill, and a postcard calling attention to the unpaid bill. Figure 6-3 shows a department store's billing reminder.

*REMEMBER TO PAY YOUR SIMPSON'S BILL . . . IT WAS DUE SEPTEMBER 10.*

**Figure 6-3**
Collection Reminder

The number of reminders a business sends can vary with the size of the debt and the debtor's payment history. If the debt is small or the debtor has a good payment history, the number of reminders will be as high as five or six. The time between reminders can vary, too. The first reminder might not be sent until the bill is 30 days past due. As the number of reminders increases, the time between them decreases. During the last segment of the reminder stage, messages might be sent every two or three days.

**APPEAL.** If reminders don't persuade the debtor to pay, the writer moves to the next stage, appeal. The writer carefully chooses the appeal that will have the greatest effect on the reader. The appeal could be to the reader's pride, sense of duty, desire to have good credit, or a combination of these. The appeal is introduced in the opening paragraph and developed in the middle section of the message.

The approach taken in the closing section of the letter depends on whether the message is in the first or the last stage of appeal. At first, the writer will push for a reason why payment has been delayed. Later, the writer will ask the reader to pay something, even a small amount, against

*Send gentle reminders.*

**&&**Never completely encircle your enemy. Leave him some escape, for he will fight even more desperately if trapped. **&&**

Alex Haley

*You can send more than one reminder.*

*When reminders are unsuccessful, use appeals.*

*Chapter 6: Writing Persuasive Messages*

the debt. The writer can also invite the reader to call or visit to work out a repayment plan. Figure 6-4 shows a collection message in the appeal stage.

## Annotations

1. Appeal
2. Details
3. Call for Action

**Dental Associates**
679 Alworth Road
Salina, KS 59772
(316) 555-4992

August 3, 20—

Mr. Kenneth J. Lopper
577 Mason Place, Apt. 445
Atlanta, GA 14533

Dear Mr. Lopper:

**1** On March 17, one of our dentists gave you her immediate attention. Now, Mr. Lopper, it's time for you to give us your immediate attention.

**2** When you visited our dental clinic, you were in pain. Your gums were bleeding and inflamed. Your tooth, you said, was throbbing badly. Because you required immediate care, patients who had scheduled appointments were asked to wait while Dr. Sherbloom and her assistant tended to your needs. The patient information form you completed and signed indicated that you would be responsible for the entire bill. Therefore, the bill for your care was mailed to you. Neither the bill nor the three reminders we've sent have prompted you to pay. Why, Mr. Lopper?

**3** If you are unable to pay the entire $345 now, pay what you can. Then, phone me to arrange a payment plan. We want only what you owe us, Mr. Lopper . . . your immediate attention to the enclosed bill.

Yours truly,

Mark Gui
Billing Clerk

Figure 6-4
Appeal-Stage Collection Letter

*When gentler attempts to collect fail, issue a warning.*

WARNING. In the warning stage, the writer *demands* action. Several weeks, perhaps months, have passed. Gentle reminders and polite requests have failed. The only tactic left is strength. The writer clearly and honestly presents the action that will be taken if payment is not received. A short deadline is set before the debt is referred to a lawyer or collection agency. Figure 6-5 shows a warning-stage collection message.

October 1, 20—

Mr. Kenneth J. Lopper
577 Mason Place, Apt. 445
Atlanta, GA 14533

Dear Mr. Lopper:

You've given us no choice. Your account must be referred to a collection agency.

We didn't want this to happen, Mr. Lopper, did you? We acted in good faith when we cared for you on March 17 when we provided you with the emergency dental care you needed. We believed you would pay us for the professional care you received. We were wrong. You've ignored bills, reminders, and appeals for payment.

If you haven't paid us the $345 you owe by October 7, we will refer your account to the Brothers Agency. It's your choice, Mr. Lopper.

Yours truly,

Marc Gui, Billing Clerk

**Figure 6-5**
Warning Stage Collection Message

## Proposals

A business proposal is a special, more advanced type of persuasive message. It is designed to define and offer a solution to a problem.

**TYPES OF BUSINESS PROPOSALS.** Proposals may be internal, external, solicited, or unsolicited.

*Internal.* These proposals are designed to solve a problem in an organization. Procedure changes, policy modifications, equipment acquisition, and employee incentives illustrate internal proposal topics. These proposals, which may be submitted as memos or reports, are directed to managers or management/staff teams that have the authority to approve and fund them.

*External.* These proposals are written for an audience outside the organization. The readers could be affiliated with a foundation or other philanthropic group, a government agency, or a for-profit organization such as a bank. Proposals to establish a seniors' center, sponsor an afternoon reading program for elementary students, and conduct research related to cancer illustrate external proposal topics. The business plan an entrepreneur submits to a financial institution or group of investors also falls into this category. These proposals, which will be read by panels internal or external to the funding source, can be formatted as letters or reports.

*Solicited.* These proposals are written in response to a **request for proposal (RFP)** or **request for bid (RFB)**. The request gives specific information about what will be funded or purchased, guidelines to be followed in preparing the proposal or bid, and information about when and to whom to send the completed document. Some RFPs also require the writer to complete and submit an application form. To view an RFP, access the Web site at *http://www.gsa.gov*, do a site search for RFP, and download one or more requests.

*Unsolicited.* These proposals are submitted solely on the writer's initiative. In a business environment, a worker might submit an outline or text summary of a proposal and then meet with a manager to get an indication of whether she/he is aware of a problem or is receptive to a particular solution. If the manager says "Expand it and put it in writing," a detailed written proposal is prepared. External agencies sometimes encourage groups to submit pre-proposals before developing full proposals.

**PARTS OF A BUSINESS PROPOSAL.** Every proposal contains some or all of the following parts:

*Title.* The proposal title should be brief and descriptive. Try to keep the title to ten or fewer words. Use action verbs and nouns. A creative title can capture a reader's attention.

*Proposals offer solutions to problems.*

*Proposals can have one or several readers.*

**❝The power of a movement lies in the fact that it can indeed change the habits of people. This change is not the result of force but of dedication, of moral persuasion. ❞**

Steven Biko

*An introductory memo or pre-proposal can be useful.*

*Abstract or Executive Summary.* This section provides an overview of the subject, purpose, activities, and outcomes. A 200–250 word, 10–15 sentence paragraph will acquaint the reader with the topic and stimulate interest in it.

*Introduction/Problem Statement.* These parts can be addressed separately or in one section. The introduction should give a sense of the problem and its history. It should establish a need and hold the reader's interest. A literature review or results of a pilot project would also be included in this section. The problem statement should provide a conceptual, broad-based framework for the goals of the project. *Employee retention* is an example of a problem.

*Objectives.* The specific, achievable, *measurable* outcomes of the proposal are its objectives. *Increase retention of computer programmers by 25 percent by the end of the fiscal year* is an objective.

*Methods/Activities.* This section describes your implementation procedures. It answers the questions *what? when?* and *why?* A well-organized action plan will boost the desire to fund the project.

*Evaluation.* Show the reader that you are serious about assessing outcomes and making appropriate modifications to ensure success. State what data you plan to gather and when they will be collected. Tell the reader how you will analyze the data and report results. Focus on continuous improvement.

*Budget.* Readers will want to know how you plan to spend their money. Include cost estimates for personnel (salaries and fringe benefits) and non-personnel (space, equipment, supplies, travel). Be honest and realistic. Avoid the tendency to inflate or understate expenses. Identify confirmed funding sources if you have them.

*Future Funding.* Tell the reader how you plan to fund the project after the requested funds have been depleted.

*Appendices.* Background information or supporting documents should be included as appendices. Keep the text of the proposal brief and focused.

*Personnel.* Include brief resumes for people who are involved with the project. Show the reader that you and your collaborators have the qualifications to make what you propose happen.

*Chapter 6: Writing Persuasive Messages*

# PROPOSAL ELEMENTS

Create the following for a proposal describing a program to improve attendance among the servers at the restaurant you manage:

Title:

Problem
Statement:

Objective:

Methods/Activities:

Evaluation:

A network of Small Business Development Centers (SBDC) exists throughout the country. Staff at SBDC locations provide no- or low-cost access to professionals who assist with activities such as developing business plans.

BUSINESS PLAN. This is a special-purpose proposal submitted to a financial institution for the purpose of creating or expanding a business. The components of a business plan are similar to those of a proposal:

*Introduction/Summary.* A concise description of the business and its proposed location; how much funding you need and why; and the time period in which money is needed.

*Ownership/Management/Employee Data.* A description of the proposed structure and information about the experience, skills, training, and qualifications of key personnel.

*Product/Service/Market Identification.* Products and services are described and differentiated from the competition. The market is defined and a marketing strategy is presented. Sales forecasts based on market research, actual or expected orders, and comparative pricing are provided.

*Administration/Production Factors.* This is information about equipment and facilities, production techniques, quality control mechanisms, management structure, and accounting systems and controls.

*Growth and Development Plans and Potential.* A one- or two-year projection linked to improvement/expansion of products, services, or markets; changes in required staffing; and additional investment.

*Financial Information.* Information about how much the project will cost, what will be provided, what is needed, and what financial security you can offer lenders.

*Appendices.* Documents that relate to or further explain/support the plan.

# Keys to Writing Effective Proposals and Business Plans

Proposals, like other forms of business writing, should reflect the 4Cs of business communication and show evidence of thorough planning. In addition, proposals should:

- Strictly adhere to the guidelines of the funding agency.

- Use side heads and clear transitions to guide the reader.

- Use lists to break text and highlight important points.

- Keep visuals to a minimum by using them only to enhance and explain abstract concepts and relationships.

- Address potential problems, do not avoid them.

- Avoid using jargon unless the terms have been precisely defined.

- Show genuine enthusiasm for the project.

- Be free of typographical, grammatical, and content errors.

> **❝ The Kellogg Foundation is able to fund only a very small percentage of the requests it currently receives. Many requests are declined, not because they are lacking in merit, but because they do not match the current programming interests of the Kellogg Foundation, or they do not fall within our programming guidelines. ❞**
>
> *http://www.wkkf.org/HowToApply/Default.asp*

# CHAPTER SUMMARY

- Persuasive messages are written using the indirect approach.

- Using *attention*, *interest*, *desire*, and *action* (AIDA) makes the indirect approach work in persuasive messages.

- Persuasive messages include sales messages, requests, claims, collection messages, and proposals.

- Sales messages differ from other persuasive messages in their length and in their use of enclosures, unconventional grammar/punctuation, and visual devices.

- Requests should stress reader benefit and give relevant details.

- Persuasive claims explain the situation, stress any positive aspect of the situation, and ask for a reasonable adjustment.

- Collection messages progress through three stages: reminder, appeal, and warning.

- Proposals define and offer a solution to a problem.

- Proposals may be internal or external and either solicited or unsolicited.

- A proposal consists of the following parts: title, abstract or executive summary, introduction/problem statement, objectives, methods/activities, evaluation, budget, future funding, appendices, and personnel.

- A business plan is a special purpose proposal consisting of an introduction/summary, ownership/management/employee data, product/service/market identification, administration/production factors, growth and development plans and potential, financial information, and appendices.

- Effective proposals and business plans adhere to the principles of good writing.

# CHAPTER 6 APPLICATIONS

**SECTION I** ***Work-related Messages.*** The following exercises require you to apply the indirect plan. Read the directions carefully. Unless specified in the text or by your instructor, you may choose the usage style you prefer (refer to Appendix A). Apply the 4Cs of communication covered in Chapter 3, and proofread for content and mechanics.

1. You have been hired to raise money to restore the Avalon Theater in your town. The people you work for plan to overhaul the 90-year old theater, which has been empty for nearly a decade. The plan is to convert the old theater into a forum for American and foreign films, for concerts, and for live theater performances. You are ready to ask residents to contribute money to fix the Avalon's seats. A contribution of $45 will restore one seat. Your task is to write a message asking people to restore one or more of the seats or to donate whatever they can to the project. Those who contribute $45 or more will receive a $15 reduction in the cost of a season ticket to the first year's events.

   a. Who will read your message?

   b. What appeal will you use?

   c. What ideas will you use to create interest?

   d. What details will you use to build desire?

   e. What action will you ask for?

   f. Will you set a deadline for action? If yes, what?

   g. Are enclosures needed? If so, what?

   h. Using the notes you made in items a–g above, write the message on a separate sheet of paper.

*Chapter 6: Writing Persuasive Messages*

## Sales Messages

2. You are a real estate agent who wants to increase the number of houses you sell. Each time you sell a home, you write to other homeowners in the area asking whether they are interested in selling their homes and encouraging them to work with you. Prepare the form letter you will use. Your company offers clients the following services: market evaluation, open houses, and advertising.

3. Your company, The Fruit Factory, places flyers like the one below next to the cash register in its store. The flyers have created some interest in your products, but not enough. You suggested that sales letters be prepared and sent to businesses listed with the local Chamber of Commerce. Your supervisor liked the idea and asked you to draft the message. Do so, and e-mail it to your instructor.

*The Fruit Factory*
*567 Orchard Drive*
*Muncie, IN 33489-5670*

Here are just a FEW of the MANY gift ideas
for customers, employees, and associates
from THE FRUIT FACTORY

a. The Morning Glory. ($8)

   Two 12-oz. bottles of syrup; one blueberry, one blackberry.

b. The Two-Tea Fruity. ($6)

   A 2-oz. jar of raspberry jam and two packages of raspberry tea.

c. The Fruit Fancy. ($14)

   A 6-oz. package of blueberry pancake mix, a 10-oz. package of blueberry muffin mix, and a 12-oz. bottle of blueberry syrup.

d. Deluxe Berry Basket. ($20)

   Two jams (2-oz. each) and two syrups (12-oz. each) of your choice (strawberry, cherry, blueberry, blackberry, raspberry).

We can customize any gift with your personalized message. We can handle any and all shipping arrangements. We can guarantee delivery by the date you need the packages. We can use your logo and/or company name if you like.

(555) 555-1066

4. The bank at which you work offers safety deposit boxes. The boxes are available in four sizes. Bank patrons lease the box on a year-to-year basis. An annual fee is charged; bills are sent one month before the leases expire. The bank has decided to raise the box fee. The sizes, current fees, and new fees are:

| | | |
|---|---|---|
| 2″ × 5″ box | $10.00 | $12.50 |
| 4″ × 6″ box | $12.50 | $15.00 |
| 6″ × 10″ box | $18.00 | $22.00 |
| 8″ × 12″ box | $25.00 | $30.00 |

Write to bank patrons who currently do not lease a safety deposit box. Persuade them to take advantage of the service. Patrons receive two keys to their box. The renters' signatures are kept on file. People are allowed entry to their boxes only after presenting their keys and having their signatures matched against the signature file.

### Requests

5. A policy at your company states that employees who have been with the firm one year are entitled to one week of paid vacation and those who have been with the firm two to five years get two weeks' paid vacation. Your two-year anniversary isn't until September 12, but you hope to persuade your employer to permit you to take it August 1–14 when you plan to go to Ireland to compete in the Dublin Marathon.

6. The fax machine in your office needs to be replaced. Do the research necessary to persuade your manager to purchase a particular make and model. Prepare an appropriate memo.

7. Your community hosts an in-line skating marathon (26.2 miles) each June. Hundreds of volunteers are needed to make the event a success. Volunteers are needed to:

- work at the registration tables.
- serve water at the rest stops.
- take numbers at the finish line.
- issue T-shirts to the finishers.
- work at the post-race refreshment tent.

The local newspaper has donated 1/4 page in the sports section and will print your message calling for volunteers. As staff coordinator for the race, write the message.

8. You are an active member of an association related to your field of study. Your local chapter will host the organization's regional conference this spring. Your task is to get items to put in the hospitality packets that will be given to each person who attends the regional meeting. The Krispy Potato Chip company is based in your town. Write to request that they donate 300 packages of their chocolate-covered ripple chips.

9. Write a message persuading the mayor of your community to spend an hour in the dunk tank at the city festival on July 4.

### Claims

10. The hotel stay associated with a recent business trip was plagued with problems. The reservation request you faxed to the hotel clearly showed you expected to arrive for your one-night stay at 2 AM June 10. The confirmation notice you received also showed June 10, but when you tried to check in, you were told there were no rooms available and you should have listed June 9 as your arrival date. After a lengthy discussion with the night manager, you were given a room with the hope that the person who had really reserved it didn't arrive. You had a fitful night's sleep because of the constant traffic to and from the vending and ice machines located near your room. You phoned the desk to complain but were told that hotel guests have a right to use the vending machines. You didn't have time to talk to the hotel manager before you left for your meetings the next day. Write a request for a refund of the $148.95 you paid for your room.

11. The printer delivered 4,000 copies of your company's annual report this morning. Much to your disappointment, the colors are not as vivid as you expected them to be and the graphs appear to have light shadows behind the lines. The reports are scheduled to be mailed to shareholders in ten days. Neither problem was detectable in the proofs you approved; other projects completed with this printer have been excellent. Persuade the printer to redo the reports at no charge.

12. Last year, your company bought five industrial vacuum cleaners for your custodial staff. Yesterday, the staff supervisor told you that cords on two of the machines were frayed because of a defect in the rewind mechanism. When he tried to order replacement rewind units, which were not covered under warranty, he learned that they were no longer made. You agree with his conclusion that parts should be available for machines that are less than a year old. Write a claim to the manufacturer.

13. Your company uses a computer-generated reminder as the first step in its collection process. It's now ready to add a second "reminder." A member of the art department has prepared the designs shown below. Select the design you would use on a postcard and write the message that will accompany it. Space is limited; you must be brief.

14. Ben Reynolds has been shopping at your family-owned clothing store for more than 40 years. Three months ago, he bought a suit and accessories to wear at his granddaughter's wedding. You haven't seen him since. He hasn't paid the $547 bill or responded to the reminders you've sent. You've tried phoning, but no one answers and there is no answering machine. Prepare an appeal stage message.

15. Debt collectors are subject to federal and state laws regarding their collection practices. Research the topic and e-mail your instructor three Internet URLs for sites that provide information on these practices.

## Proposals

16. Working in teams of 3 or 4 as directed by your instructor, identify a problem at your school and prepare a proposal to solve it.

17. Every year, your company buys a block of 20 season tickets for a professional sporting team's events. Tickets are available to employees at no charge. Propose to the Human Resource Manager that a similar program be enacted for the local symphony.

18. Job sharing, flextime, and telecommuting are three programs that have gained popularity in recent years. Select one and prepare a preliminary proposal memo that supports its adoption in the organization where you work. Do an Internet search to identify sources of information and list them in your proposal.

19. The pet shelter where you volunteer needs new dog runs. Write a letter proposal asking a local fence supplier to donate the materials and labor to install the runs.

20. Assume you work in the accounting department of a local business. Access the Web site at URL *http://ja.org* and use the information as a resource to write a proposal to have your company sponsor a Junior Achievement group and appoint you as coordinator of the project.

**SECTION II** *Personal Business Messages.* The following exercises relate to some aspect of using the indirect approach in writing situations you might face in your personal life. Read the directions carefully. Select a letter style appropriate for a personal business message, one that includes your return address (refer to Appendix A). Be sure to follow the 4Cs of communication presented in Chapter 3. Plan before writing, and proofread for both content and mechanics.

21. You have been invited to join the local chapter of Alpha Beta Gamma (ABG), a group for business professionals. Each chapter of the group has a membership limit of just 25; the last time the local chapter accepted a member was 1993. According to the invitation, signed by Membership Chair E. Jacob Zenk, the initiation ceremony—which new members *must* attend—is scheduled for February 20. As sales manager for Falls Industries, you travel frequently. In fact, you will be out of town from February 19 through 22 meeting with an important client. You *really* want to join this group . . . so much so that you will attempt to persuade the group to modify its initiation procedures.

22. Assume that your school selects one student a year as its "Outstanding Graduate." Select one of your classmates and nominate him/her for the award. Address your message to the Selection Committee.

23. Last night you attended the local theater's production of "Fiddler on the Roof." Normally, productions at the playhouse are excellent . . . not this time. The sound system crackled during four of the musical numbers, the air conditioner wasn't working, and you snagged the sleeve of your jacket on the ragged edge of the seat arm. You were so angry you left at the intermission. You still haven't calmed down. You paid $17.50 for your ticket and you want a refund. Write to the ticket office manager and state your claim.

24. Enough is enough! For the third time this year your favorite TV show has been switched to a new day and time. Write to the network program planner to express your dissatisfaction and persuade him/her to move the show back to one of its earlier time slots.

25. As a busy student, you rely heavily on frozen food. Last night you fixed a spicy chicken and rice dinner that had been in your freezer for at least two months. When you lifted the lid, you noticed that the dinner had very little chicken; when you took the first bite, you discovered the dinner tasted bland. The *Sell by* date on the dinner passed ten days ago. Write the manufacturer to express your disappointment and request a refund. You no longer have the sales slip but think you paid $2.89 for the dinner.

*Chapter 6: Writing Persuasive Messages*

# WRITING EMPLOYMENT AND SPECIAL MESSAGES

Taping a résumé to the inside cover of a pizza delivered to a prospective employer or wearing an oversized t-shirt imprinted with an occupational goal may work for some job seekers (*303 Off-the-Wall Ways to Get a Job* by Brandon Toropov), but most people find that an application letter and résumé, submitted in traditional print or electronic form, is a better approach. Those more traditional methods are described in this chapter.

## EMPLOYMENT COMMUNICATION

Both written and oral communication play a part in helping people get jobs. Written communication is used for résumés, application letters, and other correspondence. Oral communication is used during an interview. This chapter will focus on the written communication aspects of the employment process.*

## Write a Résumé

A résumé is a description of an applicant's qualifications for employment. It introduces the applicant to the prospective employer and provides evidence to convince the reader that the applicant is competent to become an employee. The content and format of a résumé may vary, but all résumés have the following characteristics:

- *Résumés have no title.* A title is unnecessary; the reader will know what the document is.
- *Résumés are brief.* Employers skim rather than read résumés, so writers present information in phrases rather than complete sentences. A résumé should be no longer than two pages.
- *Résumés are grammatically correct.* Entries related to current activities are written in the present tense; those related to

### LEARNING OBJECTIVES

- Write a résumé that highlights your strengths.
- Compose an application letter that focuses on your qualifications.
- Write other messages associated with employment communication.
- Learn when and how to write goodwill messages.
- Differentiate between formal and informal meeting minutes.
- Write news releases.

*Some resume parts are standard.*

✤ **Research shows that managers skim resumes for about 30 seconds.**

* For more complete coverage of employment, refer to *Basics of Employment Communication* (0-538-69028-3).

previous activities are written in the past tense. Items in a vertical or horizontal list must be parallel.

- *Résumés are positive.* Highlight strengths. Choose words carefully.

- *Résumés stress transferable skills.* Skills can be gained through education, experience, or activities.

- *Résumés omit personal data.* Omit race, age, religious affiliation, height, weight, marital status, parental status, gender, or other items that are not related to the job.

- *Résumés provide evidence.* Give concrete examples to illustrate strengths. For example, working 20–30 hours a week while attending school full time and raising a family shows good time management skills. It also indicates that the applicant is responsible and ambitious.

- *Traditional résumés contain action verbs (supervise, increased, monitor, improved). Scannable résumés stress nouns (manager, accountant, computer skills, license).* Choose words used in the employer's job advertisement.

- *Traditional résumés are attractive; scannable résumés are plain.* Traditional résumés use type size/font and mechanical techniques such as upper-case letters, bold, italic, and underscore to lead the reader through the résumé and highlight important items. To be readable by the greatest number of software programs, scannable résumés should use only 10- to 14-point fonts with distinct letter separations, eliminate mechanical emphasis features other than bold, and use only one column. White paper is best for both résumé types. Mail either unfolded.

To learn whether the organization prefers a traditional or a scannable résumé, check the job announcement or phone the human resources department.

Although a résumé should be unique to the person it represents, readers expect to find certain items on every résumé they receive.

**HEADING.** The heading is the first item. Include name, mailing address, e-mail address, home phone number, and fax number (if applicable). Personal Web site URLs are being included more frequently. List your work e-mail and phone only if your employer permits you to accept personal messages. Be sure your Web site and voicemail message are professional.

**JOB OBJECTIVE.** This brief statement follows the heading. It states the type of job the applicant wants. The objective may be general or targeted to a specific job or company. An objective that is too specific may destroy the chance of employment in a related area. An objective that is too general may result in the résumé being set aside because it is vague. Statements such as *willing to travel* or *willing to relocate* can be linked to the objective.

*Employers scan résumés to increase accessibility within the organization.*

*The heading and job objective form the opening of a résumé.*

## CHECKPOINT 7-1

Are the following job objectives weak or strong? Why?

a. Objective: Secretarial position.

b. Objective: Secretarial position in a Houston bank.

c. Objective: Secretarial position in which my word processing and accounting experience would contribute to company goals and lead to professional advancement.

EDUCATION. This section presents information about post-secondary school diplomas, certificates, or degrees and when/where earned. Writers may include data about courses if they relate to the job being sought. Grades or grade point averages should be included if they reflect positively on the applicant. For most recent graduates, education will be the strongest qualification; therefore, it should appear before experience.

WORK OR OTHER EXPERIENCE. Include the name/location of the organization, employment dates, and job titles. For each job title, describe duties, responsibilities, and accomplishments. Workers who have had related and other experience separate the entries and use a descriptive heading for each. *Related Work Experience, Other Work Experience* or *Other Experience* are sample headings. An entry such as *full- and part-time jobs as food service worker, clerk, and lawn care worker* can use a variety of experience to emphasize adaptability. Write items in order of their importance to the new job, not the old job or how much time you spent doing a skill at the old job.

SPECIAL SKILLS. Special skills may be listed separately or as part of either education or experience. Include computer, foreign language, or other skills an employer would expect or that set you apart from other applicants.

ACTIVITIES AND INTERESTS. Memberships, leadership roles, hobbies, and accomplishments add zest to a résumé and can attract an employer's interest. Try to show a balance among school, civic, and personal interests and between individual and group activities. This section should be brief.

*Omit high school information unless some aspect of it strengthens your qualifications.*

*Use bullets to highlight entries.*

*Activities and interests show you are a well-rounded person.*

**REFERENCES.** References are people who can tell the potential employer about your skills, abilities, and work habits. Past or present employers, co-workers, and teachers are often used as references. It is both professional and courteous to ask permission before listing people as references. The trend is to list references only when asked to provide them and to omit *References Available Upon Request* because it is obvious.

Figures 7-1, 7-2, and 7-3 show various résumé styles and formats. Note that each résumé is designed to highlight the strengths of the applicant.

## Résumé Formats

A résumé must include all items addressed in an employer's position announcement or job listing. When unsolicited, a résumé should highlight qualifications as they relate to a professional goal. Résumés can be prepared in reverse chronological or functional format.

**REVERSE CHRONOLOGICAL.** Entries within the Education, Experience, and Activities/Interests sections are listed from present to past to highlight academic development and professional advancement.

**FUNCTIONAL.** In functional résumés, skills and accomplishments are listed before information about education and experience. Descriptive words such as *reliable, motivated, budget conscious,* and *creative* draw attention to the applicant's qualifications. Supporting evidence is drawn from across the applicant's education, work experience, and volunteer experience without stating specifically when or where it was acquired. A brief listing of education and employment is presented near the end of the résumé. People who have changed jobs often or want to change career direction find this style useful.

**SCANNABLE PAPER RÉSUMÉS.** A scannable paper résumé is a dual-purpose, hard copy résumé designed to be visually appealing; to be delivered by regular mail, by hand, or by fax; and to be scannable by computer software. A scannable résumé contains less complex formatting than a traditional résumé so that it can be scanned correctly into computers and processed by résumé-tracking programs. Although the formatting of this résumé differs from a traditional résumé, the organization is no different; it may be prepared in either reverse chronological or functional format.

**ON-LINE RÉSUMÉS.** An on-line résumé can be posted using either reverse chronological or functional format. The résumé (also called an electronic résumé) is designed to be delivered via e-mail or via an Internet résumé service. This résumé must be completely stripped of word processing codes and is, therefore, a plain-looking document. Because the applicant has no control over who accesses an on-line résumé, some professionals recommend maintaining privacy by including an e-mail address rather than a residential address in the heading.

*Software programs exist to help applicants format their résumés.*

*Link the résumé to samples of your work.*

ANDREA B. FILIPPI
_____

439 West Eighth Street
Laurel, MT 88236
(813) 555-1919
abfilippi@bigskynet.com

## OBJECTIVE

To use my accounting computer skills and knowledge to provide timely and reliable financial information for your company.

## SUMMARY OF QUALIFICATIONS

* AS degree in accounting
* Strong interpersonal skills
* Problem solving skills

* Windows 98
* Spreadsheet and Database
* html, Web design

## EDUCATION

| | |
|---|---|
| 1998 – present | Billings Technical College, Billings, MT<br>Program of Study: Accounting<br>Diploma Expected: June 2000 |
| | Financial Accounting, Computerized Accounting, Income Tax, Cost Accounting, Computer Information Systems, Management, Business Writing, Business Law |

## EXPERIENCE

| | |
|---|---|
| 1998 – present | Office Assistant, Business Department, Billings Technical College |
| Responsibilities: | Assist office personnel by keyboarding; photocopying; answering phones; and responding to questions from students, faculty, and visitors. |
| Accomplishments: | Solved problems using spreadsheet and database software; created and updated departmental web site; enhanced ability to work with different types of people in a professional setting; learned and used word processing software. |
| 1994–1997 | Retail Sales Clerk, Royal Drug Store, Billings, MT |
| Responsibilities: | Completed cash and credit transactions; helped customers select and purchase products; built and maintained positive customer relations; stocked shelves. |
| Accomplishments: | Developed an understanding of the retail sales process; learned to operate a POS terminal; learned importance of inventory control. |

**Figure 7-1A**
Two-page Reverse Chronological Résumé, Page 1

**ANDREA B. FILIPPI**

## EXPERIENCE (continued)

| | |
|---|---|
| 1996–1997 | Driver, Angelo's Pizza, Billings, MT |
| Responsibilities: | Used personal auto to take fresh, hot product to location specified by customer. |
| Accomplishments: | Learned importance of planning and organizing; developed ability to work effectively in a time-pressure situation; completed more than 1,200 deliveries without having an accident. |

## ACTIVITIES/INTERESTS

| | |
|---|---|
| Volunteer usher, Billings Technical College | 1998–present |
| Member, Accounting Club, Billings Technical College | 1999–present |
| Accounting Club State Leadership Conference, 3d place, Computerized Accounting | 1999 |
| Parasailing; bridge | |
| Play city league volleyball | |

## REFERENCES

Ms. Melina Will
Office Supervisor
Business Department
Billings Technical College
6677 Birch Road
Billings, MT 60101
(813) 555-0772

Mr. Angelo Grimaldi
Owner
Angelo's Pizza
165 South Main Street
Billings, MT 60126
(813) 555-5724

Mr. Kyle Paulson
Manager
Royal Drug Store
Antler Mall
Billings, MT 60112
(813) 555-4831

Ms. June Hilsen
Accounting Instructor
Billings Technical College
6677 Birch Road
Billings, MT 60101
(813) 555-0778

**Figure 7-1B**
Two-page Reverse Chronological Résumé, Page 2

Qualifications of
MYRON BAKER WILSON
for the position of
SALES REPRESENTATIVE with ZENITH, INC.

1530 Benson Street, Apt. 228                    555-2285 (home)
Berlin, NH 21774-3614                            555-9241 (work)

## QUALIFICATIONS

Experienced Sales Associate     Six years of retail sales experience
                                Choose merchandise; create displays
                                Help customers find products to meet
                                    their needs
                                Suggest companion or complementary
                                    products

Motivated                       Promoted to Department Manager after
                                    only two years
                                Rearranged display area for improved
                                    traffic flow
                                Associate of the Month three times

Organized                       Schedule 3 full-time and 8 part-time
                                    employees
                                Coach daughter's T-ball team
                                Worked full-time while completing
                                    AA degree
                                Chaired Student Coalition child care
                                    committee

Effective Communicator          Conduct seasonal product-use seminars
                                Trained sales associates to use POS
                                    terminal
                                Prepared handout describing "special
                                    order" policy
                                Presented Child Care Center proposal to
                                    college administrative committee

**EMPLOYMENT**                            **EDUCATION**

Monroe Department Store         Evergreen Community College, Gorham, NH
Hilltop Mall                    Associate of Arts in Marketing
Berlin, NH                      May 2000
1993 to present

**Figure 7-2**
Functional Résumé

RAE LYNNE CONRAD
4501 Wilson Place
Sarasota, FL 33799-1128
(318) 555-3851

OBJECTIVE

A part-time receptionist position in a progressive metropolitan hospital or clinic.

EDUCATION

Chambers Business University, Bradenton, FL
Medical Secretary Program
Certificate to be Awarded February 2000

SPECIAL SKILLS

Keyboarding; text accuracy 95% at 55 wpm
Keyboarding; statistics accuracy 95% at 25 wpm
Windows 98, word processing, desktop publishing, WWW, html, spreadsheet, database
CPR certification

Classes in Medical Terminology, Microcomputer Systems, Machine Transcription, Word Processing, Medical Records Administration, and Business Communication.

WORK EXPERIENCE

Jake's Café, Sarasota, FL
Hostess, Cashier, Scheduler
Server and Table Clearer

ACTIVITIES AND INTERESTS

CBU Business Club Secretary 1997–98
Bradenton Community Hospital Hospice Volunteer 1994–97
Cycling, softball, and handcrafts

REFERENCES

References may be obtained by writing or phoning:
Placement Office
Chambers Business University
672 Elizabeth Street
Sarasota, FL 33755-4697
(318) 555-6789

**Figure 7-3**
Scannable Résumé

# Application Letters

An application letter accompanies a résumé and provides additional information about the applicant's employment qualifications. Like résumés, application letters are expected to reflect the background and personality of the job seeker. The characteristics of an application letter are:

*Application letters complement and supplement résumés.*

- *Application letters are brief.* Keep the letter to one page.

- *Application letters parallel résumés.* The résumé and the letter should follow the same organizational plan. If education is listed first in the résumé, it should be developed first in the letter. The letter and résumé should be worded differently. Use the letter to expand upon what was presented in the résumé.

- *Application letters refer to résumés.* The writer mentions the résumé in the text of the message and uses an enclosure notation.

- *Application letters are individually prepared.* Address the letter to the interviewer. Phone the organization to get the correct spelling and title of that person. If you are unsuccessful in identifying someone to whom to address the letter, use a general title and salutation such as *Dear Human Resource Manager* or *Dear Sales Manager.*

- *Application letters are original.* The letter should be a reflection of the writer. Use books, magazines, pamphlets, or messages authored by friends or relatives as guides, but do not copy them. Explain as honestly as you can why you want the specific job and how the employer will benefit from hiring you.

*Personalize the application letter.*

- *Application letters use personal pronouns.* The writer is focusing on his/her qualifications, so it is difficult not to begin every sentence with "I." For variety, the writer can:

Use an introductory word or phrase to begin the sentence.
*Currently, I . . .*
*While studying business at Bradford College, I . . .*

Make the reader the subject of the sentence.
*As you read the enclosed résumé, Ms. Axleson, . . .*

Use qualifications as the subject of the sentence.
*Energy and enthusiasm are among the qualifications I offer Wilson Flooring.*

Use passive voice.
*Practical work experience has been a valuable supplement to my academic preparation.*

The purpose of the application letter is to persuade the employer to interview the applicant. Therefore, use the AIDA plan. (See Chapter 6, pages 113–116, for a review of the AIDA plan.)

ATTENTION. The opening should state what type of job the writer wants. When writing to a company that has a job opening, begin by saying how information about the job was obtained.

> Mr. Adam Washington, a business instructor at Ruthton College, shared with me the job announcement describing the administrative assistant position available with your firm. My education and work experience will assure that I need minimal training time.

When applicants are unsure of whether an opening exists, they can begin the letter with a statement or question that includes information about their qualifications.

> Organized . . . motivated . . . educated in sales techniques . . . these are some of the qualities I would bring to the staff of Becker Brothers. When you have an opening for a sales representative, adding me to your staff will increase the energy, enthusiasm, and productivity of your force.

## CHECKPOINT 7-2

### ATTRACT ATTENTION

**Rewrite this letter segment to correct the problems you note.**

Dear Store Manager:

Last spring, you spoke to my retail management class at Wichita Technical College. I was very impressed with the information you gave us. I am now interested in a career in fashion merchandising.

**INTEREST AND DESIRE.** The attention-getting opening should provide a natural transition to the interest and desire sections of the message. Throughout the interest and desire sections of an application letter, the writer should be concerned with expanding on and providing evidence to support what is listed on the résumé.

> While employed at The Name of the Game, I had a perfect attendance record. Whenever an emergency fill-in worker or someone to stay extra hours was needed, my manager knew he could rely on me!

**ACTION.** End the message by asking the employer for an interview. Be courteous and positive. Offer to meet at the employer's convenience. Personalize the close by including the name of the reader and/or the name of the company.

> Ms. Sanchez, may we meet to discuss how my education and experience can benefit McMillan Computers? I can be reached by phone at home after 3 PM any weekday and can be available for an interview at your convenience.

## Letter Format

Application letters are formatted as personal business letters. Use the same size and quality stationery for the letter and the résumé. The writer's return address can be part of the signature or above the date. Figure 7-4 on the next page shows the information above the date.

*Application letters should have a professional appearance.*

## CHECKPOINT 7-3

### SELECTING SUPPLIES

Is it appropriate for a worker to use his/her employer's letterhead stationery for a letter of application? Why or why not?

5719 Hartley Court, Apartment 6
Arlington, VA 12005-6249
April 17, 20--

Mr. Alex Billowby
Human Resource Manager
Major Publishing Company
1225 C Street SW
Washington, DC 10015-3157

Dear Mr. Billowby:

Your ad in the April 16 edition of the Capital Tribune describes the qualities you seek in an editorial assistant. I believe I possess those qualifications and wish to apply for the position.

In June I will complete the requirements for a certificate in the two-year Office Technician program at Blake Business Academy. My courses have provided me with a solid background in computing, keyboarding, and writing. I am familiar with Windows and am proficient with word processing, spreadsheet, graphics, and database software. I am able to key straight copy text at 65 wpm with 95 percent accuracy. My oral and written communication skills are strong.

Practical work experience supplements my education. My part-time position at Arco Insurance as a typist/receptionist has given me valuable experience in setting priorities and meeting deadlines. Working with clients enabled me to enhance my human relations skills.

The enclosed resume provides more information about my education and work experience and describes the activities in which I have been involved. My volunteer work with the Girls' Club of Arlington has been especially rewarding and has enhanced my ability to plan and to be a contributing member of a team.

Mr. Billowby, I am eager to discuss with you how my skills and abilities might be put to work as an editorial assistant at Major Publishing. I will call you next week to request an appointment, or you may reach me at (212) 555-1528. I am looking forward to meeting you.

Sincerely,


Dawn Lubinsky

Enclosure

**Figure 7-4**
Application Letter

# Proofread

Before you mail your application letter and résumé, proofread it at least twice. Have someone whose judgment you trust review the documents. Organizations receive applications from *many* qualified applicants. An error, even a small one, can eliminate job seekers before they get an interview.

*Accuracy is critical.*

# What Happens Next?

Several things can happen after you mail your letter and résumé to a potential employer. You may receive an acknowledgment. You may be asked to complete an application form. You may be invited for an interview.

If you haven't heard anything for two weeks after the application deadline, it would be appropriate to phone or write the employer to ask about the status of your application.

Interview invitations are usually extended by phone.

If an employer sends you an application form, complete and return it promptly. Read the instructions carefully. To avoid making content errors, photocopy the form and fill in all required information on the copy first. If the instructions say to handwrite your responses, do it in black ink. The space provided for responses is usually quite small; good handwriting is essential. Put a blank sheet of paper between the pages of a multi-page form before you complete it to stop images from shadowing onto other pages. When a question does not apply to you, write N/A (not applicable) to show the employer that you read the question. Sign your complete legal name.

Respond to all questions on an application form.

Interviewers may verify the information provided on the résumé and in the application letter. They will assess your ability to communicate clearly, think logically, behave professionally, and be well mannered socially. The employer will gather information about these qualities by asking questions, listening to responses, and observing the interviewee.

## Other Employment Messages

Two additional messages deserve mention here because they relate to the job search. They are **reference requests** and **interview follow-ups**. Thank you letters will be covered in the section on Goodwill Messages.

**REFERENCE REQUESTS.** Always ask permission before including the name of a reference on your résumé or an application form. When a written request is used, organize the message by the direct approach. Indicate you are seeking a particular type of employment and ask permission to list the recipient as a reference. If the person is unfamiliar with your qualifications, explain them or enclose your résumé.

Help your references help you.

Follow-up after an interview.

**INTERVIEW FOLLOW-UP LETTERS.** Within five days after an interview, send a follow-up letter to the people you met. A follow-up message shows good business and social skills.

The message should be brief, organized by the direct approach, and prepared on the same size and quality paper used for the application letter and résumé.

Begin by thanking the interviewer for meeting with you. Include the date of the interview and indicate the specific job for which you applied. In the second paragraph, remind the employer of your strongest qualifications. If the interviewer was impressed by a particular item in your background, mention it in your follow-

# @ % $ ! # % @

Accountemps founder Robert Half describes careless mistakes in job-search documents as Resumania. Here are some samples:
- I have lurnt Word Perfect 6.0, computor, and spreadsheat programs
- Received a plague for salesperson of the Year.
- Wholly responsible for two (2) failed financial institutions.
- Completed 11 years of high school.

*USA Today* (Magazine), No. 2638, vol. 127, Pg. 10.

June 1, 20--

Mr. Alex Billowby
Human Resource Manager
Major Publishing Company
1225 C Street SW
Washington, DC 10015

Dear Mr. Billowby:

Thank you for meeting with me on Friday, May 28, to discuss the editorial assistant position available at Major Publishing. I appreciate the time you took to explain the job and the qualifications you are seeking in a person to fill it.

As we discussed during the interview, my education and work experience provide me with a solid foundation from which to begin employment. My keyboarding skills, my proficiency with various computer software programs, and my ability to communicate effectively would be assets in the job.

Mr. Billowby, I am very interested in working for Major Publishing. If there is any additional information I can provide to convince you that I'd be a productive editorial assistant, please let me know. If another interview would be useful, I'll be happy to come at your convenience. I look forward to hearing from you and to the possibility of joining the editorial staff.

Sincerely,


Dawn Lubinsky
5719 Hartley Court
Apartment 6
Arlington, VA 12005-6249
(212) 722-2428

**Figure 7-5**
Interview Follow-up Letter

*Courtesy is never out of style.*

up. If you can, provide information that will overcome any perceived weakness. Conclude the message by expressing your continued interest in the position. Figure 7-5 shows an interview follow-up letter.

# GOODWILL MESSAGES

It is always good business practice to take advantage of opportunities to be courteous to clients and colleagues. *Goodwill messages* are sent to thank, apologize, congratulate, offer sympathy, invite, welcome, or extend special greetings.

The sole purpose of a goodwill message is to make the reader feel good about an event, accomplishment, or award being recognized. Attempts to sell products or promote services can cheapen or defeat this purpose.

Goodwill messages can be handwritten, printed, or sent electronically. The formality of the message varies with the occasion and with the relationship between the sender and receiver. Suppose that a businessperson extends sympathy to a co-worker whose spouse recently died. Because of the intense personal nature of the event, the sender would probably buy a sympathy card and add a handwritten message to it. If the event were a fire that destroyed a local television station, the sender might use a keyed/printed letter. A congratulatory message could be sent electronically using one of the many Internet postcard sites.

Whatever the situation, whatever the relationship between the sender and the receiver, goodwill messages are written in the direct approach and sent as soon as possible after learning of the event or accomplishment. The following paragraphs contain suggestions for writing specific types of goodwill messages.

## Appreciation

The first paragraph should contain a sincere expression of gratitude and state specifically why thanks are being extended. The middle section of the message should expand on some impressive or especially meaningful part of the situation. Gratitude can be expressed again in the close, but the wording should be different than used to open the message. When writing a thank you note to someone who wrote a reference letter for you, include a few details about where you will be working and what your job will be.

## Apology

The key to writing an apology is to tell your reader what action you are taking to prevent a repeat of the situation. Begin with an apology, describe remedial actions, and close with a positive statement about the future.

## Congratulations

Begin by extending good wishes and stating why you are congratulating the reader. Say why the reader is worthy to have received the specific award or honor. End positively. If the message is to begin and end with a congratulatory statement, vary the wording.

WORKPLACE CONNECTIONS

Using e-mail or handing a goodwill message to the receiver diminishes the positive impact of the message.

*Match the formality of your goodwill message to the receiver and the situation.*

*Vary your word choice when expressing gratitude.*

**" Gratitude is the most exquisite form of courtesy. "**

Jacques Maritain

*Choose words that comfort the reader.*

### EXTENDING CONGRATULATIONS

Specify a reason for which a businessperson might congratulate each of the following individuals:

An employee:                                          A colleague:

A customer:

## Sympathy

State your feelings early in the message. If you can and are willing to be of assistance, say so. Specific offers of help are more meaningful than general offers of assistance. End by looking positively to the future. Figure 7-6 shows a sympathy message handwritten in a card.

## Invitation

Begin by naming the event the receiver is being asked to attend. Indicate whether a guest is permitted. Those who receive the invitation will come from a variety of family situations, so phrase the invitation to apply to all readers. Include all details the receiver needs to decide whether to attend—day, date, time, place, cost. The reader might appreciate knowing whether formal, business, or casual clothing should be worn. If a reply is desired say how, to whom, and by when. Encouraging the reader to accept the invitation is one way to end the message positively.

*Pay attention to details.*

> ❝ Don't reserve your best behavior for special occasions. You can't have two sets of manners, two social codes—one for those you admire and want to impress, another for those whom you consider unimportant. You must be the same to all people. ❞
>
> Lillian Eichler Watson

Milly,

Please accept my sympathy on the death of your father. Although I never met him, I feel I know him through you. His sense of humor, his belief that hard work leads to success, and his strong commitment to his family are all reflected in you. Take comfort in knowing that your friends are and will be here to help you. If you need a babysitter while you settle estate-related matters, please call on me.

Ty

**Figure 7-6**
Sympathy Note

# Welcome

Welcome messages can be sent to new employees, new clients, or new residents of a community. Start with a warm expression of welcome and then explain why the association will be mutually beneficial. End with another expression of welcome, or build positively on some aspect of the new relationship.

*The message should be warm and friendly.*

## Special Greetings

Birthdays, weddings, anniversaries, births, and holidays are some of the special occasions that call for goodwill messages. Begin by extending greetings, add a personal statement about the event, and end positively.

---

## CHECKPOINT 7-5

### RECOGNIZING SPECIAL OCCASIONS

You are administrative assistant to the human resource manager of a large clothing manufacturing firm located in Los Angeles, California. The men and women you employ range in age from 16 to 70. Some are United States citizens, some come from other countries and have permits to work in the U.S. It's December 1, and your supervisor is considering sending a Christmas message to the plant's employees.

On a separate sheet of paper write the advice you would give your supervisor about the appropriateness of sending such a message.

---

# MINUTES OF A MEETING

Minutes provide historical and practical documentation of reports, important discussions, decisions, and announcements made during meetings. Formal minutes follow the guidelines of a parliamentary authority such as *Robert's Rules of Order*. Informal minutes follow the practice of the group or the preference of the recorder. Meeting minutes usually contain:

- Group name
- Time meeting begins and ends
- Names of leader, participants, and guests
- Action(s) taken on minutes of previous meeting(s)
- Report summaries
- Summaries of important discussions
- Follow-up assignments
- Announcements
- Name and signature of person who recorded the minutes

*Minutes provide a practical and historical record.*

Events are reported in chronological order. Motions and their results are reported exactly as stated during the meeting. The minutes are presented attractively, with side headings used to guide the reader. When distributed promptly after a meeting, minutes help plan the agenda for the next meeting and remind participants of tasks for which they are responsible. Figure 7-7 shows minutes of a company's staff council.

Staff Council
November 11, 20--
2 PM
Room 272

Present:   B. Aldof, G. Gunderson, T. Hardy, M. Prevost (Chair),
           C. Rios
Guest      G. Unger

Minutes of the November 4 meeting were approved as distributed.

**Reports**

- The worker satisfaction survey is ready for distribution. Some concern about distributing it so close to the holiday season. Moved/Seconded/Passed: The survey will be distributed as scheduled.
- G. Unger described the status of negotiations with the company's insurance carrier. Health care costs continue to rise. Additional information will be available at the next meeting.

**Old Business**

- Web site. Council would have to create and maintain its own site, but it could be posted to the company computer. C. Rios will prepare newsletter item asking for volunteer.

**New Business**

- Retirement Planning Seminar. Discussion about possibility of sponsoring one for workers. B. Aldof will investigate speakers and costs.

**Announcements**

Next meeting November 18.

Meeting adjourned at 2:35 PM

Walter Ellington, Recorder

**Figure 7-7**
Meeting Minutes

# NEWS RELEASES

*News releases are sent to print, radio, and television outlets.*

Organizations use news releases to announce good news, put a positive slant on bad news, and reassure the public in times of crisis. Follow these guidelines when preparing a news release to be sent to representatives of the print and electronic media:

- Place the name and phone number of the organization's contact at the top of the first page.

- Put the date and the name of the city from which the release originates near the top of the first page.

- Use an attention-getting opening, called a **lead,** that briefly states what the news is.

- Answer *who? what? when? where? why?* and *how?* in a sequence that puts the most important items first. If editors and announcers are short of space or time, they will cut text from the end.

- Use short sentences and simple words.

- Make the release easy to read and edit by formatting in double space. Put - MORE - at the bottom of every page that is to be continued, and center - 30 - or ### below the last line of the release to show the end.

The competition for column inches and air time is great. Writers can increase the chances of having their releases selected for print or broadcast by addressing their copy to a specific editor or program manager and writing for the particular print or broadcast audience the receiver represents. Figure 7-8 shows a news release.

Contact:    Marv Carter
654.555.6877    **FOR IMMEDIATE RELEASE**

**DENISE RAU NAMED CHIEF EXECUTIVE OFFICER
OF WEBSTER INTERNATIONAL**

**Rochester, MN, September 3, 2000.** Denise Rau has been named Chief Executive Officer of Webster International, the region's leading producer of cold weather footwear.

Rau joined Webster in 1981 after earning her BS degree in Finance from State University. Since then, she has held a variety of posts, most recently Executive Vice President.

In announcing the appointment, Webster's Board Chairman, Edwin Somerset said, "Denise has the energy and ideas to propel Webster into the future. Her experience and her commitment to the company and the people of this region make her an outstanding choice for this important role."

Rau is active in Leaderhsip Rochester, serves on the symphony board, and volunteers with the hospice at County General Hospital.

Rau resides in Rochester with her husband Fred and their three children.

**Figure 7-8**

# CHAPTER SUMMARY

- Employment communication involves both written and oral communication.

- A résumé and application letter persuade a potential employer to interview an applicant.

- Résumés are brief, grammatically correct, positive documents that stress transferrable skills and provide evidence the applicant has them.

- Personal data is omitted from a résumé.

- Traditional and scannable résumés are similar in content but different in format.

- Résumés consist of a heading; a job objective; and sections about education, experience, special skills, and activities/interests.

- Names of references are provided only when requested.

- Résumés can be formatted reverse chronologically or functionally. Both formats work for on-line entry.

- Application letters are brief, individually prepared, original messages that complement résumés.

- Résumé writers may use the personal pronoun "I" but vary sentence structure to avoid overemphasizing it.

- Application letters follow the AIDA plan for persuasive messages and are formatted as personal business letters.

- Proofreading is essential; a typographical error can eliminate an applicant from consideration for a job.

- After sending a letter and résumé, applicants:
  - might receive an acknowledgment.
  - should inquire if no response is received in two weeks.
  - could receive a call inviting them for an interview.

- Reference requests and interview follow-up letters are employment-related messages.

- Goodwill messages are used to bring social warmth to the business environment; their sole purpose is to make the reader feel good.

- Appreciation, apology, congratulations, sympathy, invitation, welcome, and special greetings are goodwill messages.

- Goodwill messages are organized by the direct approach.

- Minutes provide a historical and practical record of what happened at a meeting.

- News releases attract the attention of the media and help an organization announce good news, present bad news positively, and manage a crisis.

words@work  Go to the Workplace Writing Tab; access and read the lesson on Finding a Job. Complete the appropriate *words@work* exercises.

# CHAPTER 7 APPLICATIONS

1. Find an employment ad/announcement in your local paper or on the Internet. Prepare a résumé that you can use to apply for the job. Attach a copy of the ad/announcement with your résumé when you submit it to your instructor.

2. Convert the résumé prepared in Application 1 to scannable format.

3. Using the ad or advertisement you clipped from the newspaper, prepare a letter of application that responds to it.

4. Select a company for which you would like to work. Assume that you don't know whether the company has an opening. Prepare an appropriate letter of application.

5. Use your résumé to help you complete the application form printed on pages 161–164.

6. Select a former teacher or employer and prepare a letter asking permission to list the person as a reference.

7. Assume that you were interviewed for a job. Prepare a follow-up letter to send to the interviewer.

8. You've been hired for the job! Write to thank the person in item 6 who gave you a reference.

9. You work in the circulation department of your local newspaper. Recently, the department bought a computerized billing system. Shortly after the system was put into use, calls and letters came pouring in from customers complaining because they received their bills after the suggested payment date. Your supervisor, Mel Remfro, has decided the most efficient way to respond and avoid future complaints is to print an apology in the next 10 editions of the paper. He's asked you to edit his message (shown below) for content and mechanics. Send your revision to Mel (your instructor) by e-mail.

> Dear Loyal Subscribers,
>
> It seems to me that we've created a major problem with our new, highly efficient client billing system which causes our customers to receive their monthly or quarterly billings statements AFTER the date suggested for payment on the bill. I understand why your angry. Believe me, if I was on the recieving end of those bills I'dbe mad as a wet hen-as many of your are.
>
> I APOLOGY!!!
>
> Please accept this sincere apology for this mistake. The problem will be solved. We've called the company that sold use the package, and they have assured us the solution is simply and the problem will be corrected by the end of the month. Please call me if you have questions.
>
> Yours very sincerely,
>
> Mel Remfro, Circulation Manger

10. It's 2 PM Friday. You returned to your office after taking notes at a luncheon meeting of the planning committee, a meeting that should have ended at 1:15 PM. You check your desk calendar and realize you missed your 1:30 appointment with Ed Duff, employee benefit specialist in the HR Department. Ed wanted to leave the office at noon but stayed because you wanted to meet with him. You phone his office and learn that he has left. The secretary also tells you that it's not unusual for Ed to come to the office on weekends. The appointment can be rescheduled, but you feel you owe Ed an apology for missing the meeting. You decide to send him (your instructor) an e-mail.

11. One of the pleasures of being employed by Prestige Publishers is working with Vince Bydalek. Vince is a friendly, optimistic man who makes the darkest situation seem bright and the most complex problem simple. He trained you on your first job and recommended you for promotion to your current position. Yesterday, Vince had a heart attack. He's doing well but will be in the hospital for at least a week and out of work for six to eight weeks.

   a. You've purchased a get well card to send to Vince. Handwrite a personal note in the space below.

*T hinking of you
and hoping that each new day
will find you feeling better.*

b. Last night you visited Vince at his home. He tried to be cheerful, but you learned from his wife that he's discouraged because he isn't making faster progress. Also, he's not enjoying the salt-free diet the doctor placed him on. Today you purchased a card, one with a blank inside. Handwrite your message in the space below.

c. Vince had a second, fatal heart attack. Send a sympathy note to his wife.

12. Your local Chamber of Commerce recently selected two of your colleagues, Mary Ylinen and Todd Westholm to receive its Ambassador Award. The award recognizes contributions to the community and success in business. Mary is an old friend. The two of you grew up in the same neighborhood and were classmates through high school. She is supervisor of your company's travel department. She is very active in Mothers Against Drunk Driving. Todd joined your firm just three years ago. He supervises the office services division. You were both part of a cost-cutting task force last year. He is a volunteer with the American Cancer Society. Write messages congratulating Mary and Todd.

13. Access the Web site at URL *http://bluemountain.com* or search on the keyword *postcards* to locate another source of on-line greeting cards. Select one that is appropriate to thank your instructor for working with your class this term. Send the message.

14. You operate a travel agency. You recently learned that the space next to you has been leased to Margo Kelpel, who plans to operate a luggage store. Prepare a message to welcome her to the mall.

15. It's February 16, and you're happy. You can credit just one thing for your cheerful spirit—the school play you saw last night. It was delightful—due in great part, you believe, to the performance given by your eight-year-old niece, Madeleine. Despite Madeleine's incredible talent, you realize that the teacher also played a part in the play's success. Write a letter to acknowledge her contribution to the successful show.

16. Attend a meeting at your school or in your community. Record minutes for the event.

17. Prepare a news release announcing that someone in your class has been named your school's Outstanding Business Communication Student.

*Chapter 7: Writing Employment and Special Messages*

An Equal Opportunity Employer

## SOUTHEASTERN UTILITIES
10 East Halloway  Charlotte, SC  28104-1110

Last Name

First Name

Middle Initial

# APPLICATION FOR EMPLOYMENT

Please return this form to:

_____
Name of Company Representative

_____
Date of Application

Divisional Offices
Fayettville, SC
Charlotte, SC
Greenville, SC

*Instructions to Applicant:*

Fill out completely, using ink.

The information contained in this application will be considered personal and confidential and used only in conjunction with your possible employment by our Company. Please furnish us with complete information. You are encouraged to attach any additional information which you believe qualifies you for the position.

Name (Same as on Social Security Card)

_____
        Last                    First                Middle

Social Security No. _____

Temporary Address _____
                          Street      City      State      Zip

Telephone No. _____

Permanent Address _____
                          Street      City      State      Zip

Phone No. _____

How long have you lived there _____

**JOB INTERESTS**

Position desired _____

When available _____

Would you accept part-time employment? _____   Temporary employment? _____

Other positions for which you are qualified _____

Location preference or restrictions _____

Why are you seeking a job change _____

Starting salary desired _____

## EXPERIENCE

**PLEASE LIST MOST RECENT EXPERIENCE FIRST**

| Name of Employer | | Type of Business | | |
| --- | --- | --- | --- | --- |

| Street Address, City, State, Zip Code | | | Phone | |
| --- | --- | --- | --- | --- |

| Dates Employed From    To | Starting Title | Last Title | Starting Salary | Final Salary |
| --- | --- | --- | --- | --- |
| Name of Supervisor | | May we contact now? No ☐  Yes ☐ | Reason for leaving | |

Brief Description of Duties

| Full-time or part-time | If part-time, average hours per week:        hours |
| --- | --- |

| Name of Employer | | Type of Business | | |
| --- | --- | --- | --- | --- |

| Street Address, City, State, Zip Code | | | Phone | |
| --- | --- | --- | --- | --- |

| Date Employed From    To | Starting Title | Last Title | Starting Salary | Final Salary |
| --- | --- | --- | --- | --- |
| Name of Supervisor | | May we contact now? No ☐  Yes ☐ | Reason for leaving | |

Brief Description of Duties

| Full-time or part-time | If part-time, average hours per week:        hours |
| --- | --- |

| Name of Employer | | Type of Business | | |
| --- | --- | --- | --- | --- |

| Street Address, City, State, Zip Code | | | Phone | |
| --- | --- | --- | --- | --- |

| Dates Employed From    To | Starting Title | Last Title | Starting Salary | Final Salary |
| --- | --- | --- | --- | --- |
| Name of Supervisor | | May we contact now? No ☐  Yes ☐ | Reason for leaving | |

Brief Description of Duties

| Full-time or part-time | If part-time, average hours per week:        hours |
| --- | --- |

| Name of Employer | | Type of Business | | |
| --- | --- | --- | --- | --- |

| Street Address, City, State, Zip Code | | | Phone | |
| --- | --- | --- | --- | --- |

| Dates Employed From    To | Starting Title | Last Title | Starting Salary | Final Salary |
| --- | --- | --- | --- | --- |
| Name of Supervisor | | May we contact now? No ☐  Yes ☐ | Reason for leaving | |

Brief Description of Duties

| Full-time or part-time | If part-time, average hours per week:        hours |
| --- | --- |

Summarize prior relevant experience and fill in periods of unemployment or periods not accounted for above. Use a separate sheet of paper if you need more space. Also, list any volunteer experience which relates to the position for which you are applying.

## U.S. MILITARY SERVICE

Branch of Service _____

Extended Active Duty From _____ To _____

Highest Rank or Grade _____

National Guard or Reserve Duty From _____ To _____

Service Schools and other Special Training _____

Major duties _____

*Chapter 7: Writing Employment and Special Messages*

## EDUCATION AND TRAINING

| Type of School | School Name and Location | Major | Dates From | To | Years Com. | Diploma—Degree Certificate Received | Grade Avg. |
|---|---|---|---|---|---|---|---|
| High School | | | | | | | |
| College | | | | | | | |
| | | | | | | | |
| Graduate School | | | | | | | |
| Vocational, Business, Trade, or Service School | | | | | | | |

Special Skills: Type _____ wpm.   Shorthand _____ wpm.   Other (Licenses/certificates, etc.) _____

_____

_____

_____

## PERSONAL AND HEALTH

Indicate jobs held during high school and college academic year: _____

Summer jobs: _____

How much of your education did you finance? _____

High school/college honors received: _____

High school/college extra curricular activities: _____

_____

Hobbies and/or outside interests: _____

_____

_____

Have you had any convictions other than minor traffic?   Yes ☐      No ☐      If yes, what was the conviction:

_____ When: _____

(Your answer will not necessarily bar you from employment at Southeastern Utilities)

Do you have any physical or health limitations which affect your work performance?   Yes ☐      No ☐

If you have answered yes, please explain: _____

_____

Are you a Citizen of the USA?   Yes ☐      No ☐

If not, do you have the legal right to remain and work in the USA?   Yes ☐      No ☐

Is adequate transportation available to you so that you could get to work on time every day?   Yes ☐      No ☐

Is there any reason why you cannot be at work on time every day?   Yes ☐      No ☐

**REFERENCES**

Names of acquaintances who work for Southeastern Utilities at any location: _____

_____

Who referred you to Southeastern Utilities: _____

Company policy puts certain restrictions on the placement of relatives. Please give names and locations of all your relatives working at Southeastern Utilities: parents, grandparents, children, grandchildren, sisters, brothers, uncles, aunts, nieces, nephews, first cousins, spouse, mother-in-law, father-in-law, daughters-in-law, sons-in-law, brothers-in-law, and sisters-in-law.

_____

_____

_____

_____

Names of three persons who have known you well, preferably from a work environment and who can be contacted. (Do **NOT** include relatives, former employers, clergy, or employees of this Company)

| Name | Business or Profession | Street Address, City, State, Zip Code, and Phone Number |
|------|------------------------|--------------------------------------------------------|
|      |                        |                                                        |
|      |                        |                                                        |
|      |                        |                                                        |

Please write in ink in your own handwriting a short paragraph describing why you desire employment with Southeastern Utilities.

**IMPORTANT: READ BEFORE SIGNING**

The facts set forth in my application are true and complete. I understand that false statements on this application shall be considered cause for refusal of or separation from employment. I authorize investigation of all statements and matters contained in this application which Southeastern Utilities may deem relevant to my employment. I authorize all my previous employers or other persons having information concerning me or my record to report such information to Southeastern Utilities. I release Southeastern Utilities and any person providing information to Southeastern Utilities from all claims or liabilities whatsoever in connection with making such investigation or making such disclosures.

I agree to have a medical examination at Southeastern Utilities' expense by a doctor designated by Southeastern Utilities prior to final acceptance of employment, and at subsequent intervals as the employer may direct, it being understood that such medical examinations are to determine my physical fitness for employment or continued employment in the event I am employed. I further understand that if employed the Company may bond me at their expense for any amount deemed necessary.

I understand that Southeastern Utilities makes no promise or agreement to employ me for a certain period of time. If I am employed, Southeastern Utilities may terminate my employment at any time, with or without cause, for any lawful reason. Also, any Southeastern Utilities employee is free to terminate his or her employment at any time.

Signature of Applicant _____

Date _____

*Chapter 7: Writing Employment and Special Messages*

# Appendix A  Message Format Guidelines

## PERSONAL BUSINESS LETTER

### Modified Block Style

```
                              709 First Avenue South          Return
                              Dermott, AK 71638-8116          Address
                              December 7, 20—                 Date

         4 space = 3 blank lines

Mr. Alex P. Perkla                                            Letter
Homemade Construction                                        Address
576 Park Lane
Dermott, AK 71638-1209
         2 spaces = 1 blank line
Dear Mr. Perkla:                                             Salutation
         2 spaces = 1 blank line
Thank you for helping to make this year's Friends and        Body
Neighbors dinner a success.
         2 spaces = 1 blank line
The tables and benches your crews built, delivered, and
set up were put to good use. Meals were enjoyed by 376
people who might otherwise have spent their holiday
alone and hungry. The enclosed notes, written by some
of the children who attended, reflect the sentiments of
the entire group.
         2 spaces = 1 blank line
Homemade Construction has a positive reputation in the
community. That reputation is well deserved.

         2 spaces = 1 blank line
                         Sincerely

                         4 spaces = 3 blank lines

                                                             Signature
                         Chuck L. Fosgate, Chair             Lines
                         Friends and Neighbors Dinner

         2 spaces = 1 blank line                             Enclosure
Enclosures                                                   Notation
```

# BLOCK LETTER STYLE

## Mixed Punctuation

**FRIENDS AND NEIGHBORS**
P.O. Box 7201
Dermott, AK 71638-7201

Date

December 7, 20—

4 spaces = 3 blank lines

Letter
Address

Mr. Alex P. Perkla
Homemade Construction
576 Park Lane
Dermott, AK 71638-1209
2 spaces = 1 blank line

Salutation

Dear Mr. Perkla:
2 spaces = 1 blank line

Body

Thank you for helping to make this year's Friends and
Neighbors dinner a success.
2 spaces = 1 blank line
The tables and benches your crews built, delivered, and
set up were put to good use. Meals were enjoyed by 376
people who might otherwise have spent their holiday
alone and hungry.
2 spaces = 1 blank line
Homemade Construction has a positive reputation in the
community. That reputation is well deserved.
2 spaces = 1 blank line

Complimentary
Close

Sincerely,

4 spaces = 3 blank lines

Signature
Lines
Reference
Initials
Copy Notation

Chuck L. Fosgate, Chair
2 spaces = 1 blank line
vu

c Chamber of Commerce

# HEADING FOR SECOND AND ADDITIONAL PAGES OF A LETTER

1' Top Margin  = 6 blank lines

Mr. Alex P. Perkla
Page 2              (use appropriate page number)
December 7, 20—
2 spaces = 1 blank line
Body of message is continued. At least two lines
of text should be carried to continuation pages.

**FRIENDS AND NEIGHBORS**
P.O. Box 7201
Dermott, AK 71638-7201

December 7, 20—                                          Date

4 spaces = 3 blank lines

Mr. Alex P. Perkla                                       Letter
Homemade Construction                                    Address
576 Park Lane
Dermott, AK 71638-1209
    2 spaces = 1 blank line
HOLIDAY GRATITUDE    Display the subject line in capital letters    Subject Line
    2 spaces = 1 blank line
Thank you for helping to make this year's Friends       Body
and Neighbors dinner a success.
    2 spaces = 1 blank line
The tables and benches your crews built, delivered,
and set up were put to good use. Meals were enjoyed
by 376 people who might otherwise have spent their
holiday alone and hungry. The enclosed notes,
written by some of the children who attended,
reflect the sentiments of the entire group.
    2 spaces = 1 blank line
Homemade Construction has a positive reputation in
the community. That reputation is well deserved.


    4 spaces = 3 blank lines


CHUCK L. FOSGATE, CHAIR Display signature lines in capital letters    Signature
    2 spaces = 1 blank line                                      Lines
vu                                                       Reference
    2 spaces = 1 blank line                         Initials
Enclosures                                               Enclosure
                                                         Notation

# TRADITIONAL MEMO

**Memo Headings**

**Body**

**Treat enumerated items as paragraphs**

**Align text for readability**

**Reference Initials**

**Enclosure Notation**

```
        TO:  Marketing Department Staff
                 2 spaces = 1 blank line
      FROM:  Paula Pierz, Manager
                 2 spaces = 1 blank line
      DATE:  September 25, 20—
                 2 spaces = 1 blank line
   SUBJECT:  Staff Meeting
                 2 spaces = 1 blank line
             Representative of ACE Computer
             Corporation will be here October 7, 8,
             and 9 to conduct training sessions for
             us. These all-day sessions will be held
             in Conference Room A; equipment will be
             installed there for our use. Please
             bring the following materials with you:
                 2 spaces = 1 blank line
             1.  Operating system manual
                     2 spaces = 1 blank line
             2.  Graphics software manual
                     2 spaces = 1 blank line
             3.  Word processing software manual
                     2 spaces = 1 blank line
             4.  Samples of letters, memos, reports,
                 and proposals you have completed
                 during the past six months
                     2 spaces = 1 blank line
             The attached brochure will more fully
             describe the training we will receive.
             Please read it before the first
             session.
                 2 spaces = 1 blank line
             These classes will provide a good
             introduction to our equipment and
             software. It is important that we all
             attend. Sessions covering advanced
             applications will be scheduled after
             the first of the year.
                 2 spaces = 1 blank line
             eb
                 2 spaces = 1 blank line
             Attachment
```

# SIMPLIFIED MEMO

September 25, 20——

Marketing Department Staff
    2 spaces = 1 blank line
STAFF MEETING
    2 spaces = 1 blank line
Representative of ACE Computer Corporation will
be here October 7, 8, and 9 to conduct training
sessions for us. These all-day sessions will be
held in Conference Room A; equipment will be
installed there for our use. Please bring the
following materials with you:
    2 spaces = 1 blank line
1.  Operating system manual.
    2 spaces = 1 blank line
2.  Graphics software manual.
    2 spaces = 1 blank line
3.  Word processing software manual.
    2 spaces = 1 blank line
4.  Copies of three letters, three memos, two
    reports, and one proposal you have prepared
    during the past fiscal year.
    2 spaces = 1 blank line
These classes will provide a good introduction to
our equipment and software. It is important that
we all attend. Sessions covering advanced
applications will be scheduled after the first of
the year.

    4 spaces = 3 blank lines


Paula Pierz, Manager
    2 spaces = 1 blank line
eb
    2 spaces = 1 blank line
c Elsa Wilke
  Computer Committee

Body

Treat
enumerated
items as
paragraphs

Align text
for readability

Signature
Line

Reference
Initials

Copy Notation

# US POSTAL SERVICE

## STANDARD 2-LETTER MAILING ABBREVIATIONS
## STATES, DISTRICTS, AND TERRITORIES OF THE UNITED STATES

| | | | |
|---|---|---|---|
| Alabama | AL | Montana | MT |
| Alaska | AK | Nebraska | NE |
| Arizona | AZ | Nevada | NV |
| Arkansas | AR | New Hampshire | NH |
| California | CA | New Jersey | NJ |
| Colorado | CO | New Mexico | NM |
| Connecticut | CT | New York | NY |
| Delaware | DE | North Carolina | NC |
| District of Columbia | DC | North Dakota | ND |
| Florida | FL | Ohio | OH |
| Georgia | GA | Oklahoma | OK |
| Hawaii | HI | Oregon | OR |
| Idaho | ID | Pennsylvania | PA |
| Illinois | IL | Puerto Rico | PR |
| Indiana | IN | Rhode Island | RI |
| Iowa | IA | South Carolina | SC |
| Kansas | KS | South Dakota | SD |
| Kentucky | KY | Tennessee | TN |
| Louisiana | LA | Texas | TX |
| Maine | ME | Utah | UT |
| Maryland | MD | Vermont | VT |
| Massachusetts | MA | Virginia | VA |
| Michigan | MI | Washington | WA |
| Minnesota | MN | West Virginia | WV |
| Mississippi | MS | Wisconsin | WI |
| Missouri | MO | Wyoming | WY |

## STANDARD 2-LETTER ABBREVIATIONS
## CANADIAN PROVINCES

| | |
|---|---|
| Alberta | AB |
| British Columbia | BC |
| Manitoba | MB |
| New Brunswick | NB |
| Newfoundland | NF |
| Northwest Territories | NT |
| Nova Scotia | NS |
| Ontario | ON |
| Prince Edward Island | PE |
| Quebec | PQ |
| Saskatchewan | SK |
| Yukon Territory | YT |

*Appendix A: Message Format Guidelines*

# Appendix B    Editing Symbols

| Symbol | Meaning | Before | After |
|--------|---------|--------|-------|
| ≡ or *Cap* | Capitalize | j̲o̲e̲ | Joe |
| ◡ | Close | can‿not | cannot |
| ⌐⌐ | Delete | the ~~the~~ day | the day |
| … or *stet* | Don't change | ~~simple~~ plan | simple plan |
| ∧  ∨ | Insert | at ∧ time *that* ∨ shipper ∧ s | at that time shipper's |
| ⊏ | Move Left | New York ⊏Memphis | New York Memphis |
| ⊐ | Move Right | 27.16 ⊏11.12⊐ 9.03 | 27.16 11.12 9.03 |
| *lc or* / | Use lowercase | /Manager | manager |
| ◯ *sp* | Spell in full | ⟨Oct.⟩ *sp.* | October |
| # | Space | once#again | once again |
| ∽ | Transpose | to ⟨quickly go⟩ | to go quickly |
| ——— | Underline or Italics | C̲l̲o̲s̲e̲u̲p̲ | Closeup or *Closeup* |
| ¶ | Paragraph | Please let me know when you plan to arrive.¶ I am looking forward to seeing you again. | Please let me know when you plan to arrive.  I am looking forward to seeing you again. |
| *no* ¶ | No new paragraph | Please let me know when you plan to arrive. *no ¶* I will meet your flight. | Please let me know when you plan to arrive.  I will meet your flight. |

# Appendix C    Frequently Confused/ Misused Words

| | |
|---|---|
| accept | receive |
| except | other than |
| | |
| advice | words of help |
| advise | give advice or counsel |
| | |
| affect | influence |
| effect | outcome; result |
| | |
| already | before the expected time |
| all ready | fully prepared |
| | |
| alternate | a substitute; to repeatedly change from one to another |
| alternative | a choice between/among |
| | |
| among | used with three or more persons or things |
| between | used to show relationship of two persons or things |
| | |
| anyone | any person |
| any one | any one of many persons or things |
| | |
| anytime | no particular time |
| any time | an amount of time |
| | |
| anyway | in any case |
| any way | by any manner |
| | |
| assure | promise |
| ensure | be certain; safe from harm |
| insure | protect life or property from loss |
| | |
| badly | describes how a person or thing acts or behaves |
| bad | describes how a person or thing is; use bad in conjunction with the five senses—touch, taste, smell, sight, and sound |
| | |
| both | items or people considered collectively |
| each | items or people considered separately |

| | |
|---|---|
| bring | carry to the speaker or the speaker's place |
| take | carry away from the speaker or the speaker's place |
| | |
| can | ability to do something |
| may | permission; possibility |
| | |
| capital | chief or main; it may refer to the *city* where government buildings are located, to a letter, to a budget, or to a form of punishment |
| capitol | *buildings* of a state government |
| | |
| come | move toward the speaker or the speaker's place |
| go | move away from the speaker or the speaker's place |
| | |
| everyday | routine, common |
| every day | each day |
| | |
| everyone | everybody |
| every one | each one |
| | |
| farther | physical distance |
| further | additional |
| | |
| fewer | a smaller quantity or amount; used with counted things |
| less | used with singular nouns and with things that cannot be counted |
| | |
| good | describes the quality of something; only with nouns |
| well | healthy; rightly |
| | |
| irregardless | This word is considered substandard; it's a double negative |
| regardless | in spite of |
| | |
| its | possessive form of it |
| it's | contraction meaning "it is" |
| | |
| lead | metallic element |
| led | past tense of *lead* |
| | |
| lose | opposite of win |
| loose | not tight or not secure; free |
| | |
| past | at a time gone by |
| passed | moved beyond; circulated |
| | |
| personal | private |

| | |
|---|---|
| personnel | workers; employees |
| | |
| principal | main; chief |
| principle | guide; rule |
| | |
| real | true or actual; used to describe a noun or pronoun |
| really | truly or actually; used with verbs, adverbs, or adjectives |
| | |
| than | as compared to |
| then | at that time |
| | |
| their | possessive pronoun |
| there | at that place |
| they're | contraction for "they are" |
| | |
| to | used with words; indicates such things as placement or purpose |
| too | also; excessive |
| two | the number 2 |
| | |
| weather | climate |
| whether | used with stated alternatives |

# Checkpoint Solutions

## CHAPTER 1

### Checkpoint 1-1

Employers rank communication skills highly because workers need those skills to interact with others within the organization and with customers and other external constituencies. A worker may have academic credentials, but if the employee can't communicate answers or ideas to others, the credentials don't mean much.

### Checkpoint 1-2

Hopefully, you disagree. Although examples of unethical behavior may receive publicity, the vast majority of business transactions and the people who complete them are ethical.

### Checkpoint 1-3

Your response should describe a situation in which time is a major factor or one in which emotional or confidential content is involved. Both face-to-face and telephone communication facilitate speedy delivery and feedback.

## CHAPTER 2

### Checkpoint 2-1

1. General Goal(s):  Request

   Specific Goal:  Gain approval to take time off.

2. General Goal(s):  Inform

   Specific Goal:  Explain what has been done, what remains to be done, why the project isn't on schedule, and what will be done to compensate for the delays.

3. General Goal(s):    Request

   Specific Goal:    Obtain information about a regulation so that your organization may comply with it.

4. General Goal(s):    Inform/Persuade

   Specific Goal:    Provide information about current and proposed operations; persuade the lending agency to approve the loan.

5. General Goal(s):    Inform/Goodwill

   Specific Goal:    Provide information about the organization, its financial status, and what shareholders can expect in the short and long term. The report should maintain or increase current or prospective shareholders' confidence in the organization.

## Checkpoint 2-2

1. Bill:    Disappointed, perhaps embarrassed, or even a bit angry.

   Sally:    Happy; perhaps a bit apprehensive about the responsibility and challenge she faces.

2. Bill:    You might want to know about whether Bill has lost other elections during his membership in the club. Knowing his opinion of Sally and her potential as a leader would also be helpful.

   Sally:    You'll want to know whether Sally was a serious candidate or merely agreed to have her name listed to fill the ballot with no expectation of defeating a long-term member. Also, you might want to know what leadership positions she has held with other organizations.

3. The emotional aspects of the situation would be easier to handle.

## Checkpoint 2-3

1. Inform

2. Tell the patient the records have been sent; maintain goodwill.

3. Verbal (written)

4. Letter

5. Direct

6. B should be first; A should be last. The remaining items could be arranged in a variety ways.

# CHAPTER 3

## Checkpoint 3-1

1. Sample responses:
   a. yield, give in, surrender
   b. similar, compatible, matched
   c. flawless, perfect, spotless
   d. hasty, careless, reckless
   e. practical, realistic, useful
2. Sample responses:
   a. 3 a.m.
   b. over 5000
   c. 10 minutes ago
   d. 2 inches tall
   e. 6'7"

## Checkpoint 3-2

Answers will vary.

## Checkpoint 3-3

Sample responses:

   a. While waiting for the bus, I saw a limousine stop in front of the hotel.
   b. Before locking the door, the guard set the alarm.
   c. As I approached the conference room, I heard people laughing and clapping.
   d. Hardware and finances limit the amount of programming the television station can offer.
   e. Correct.

## Checkpoint 3-4

1. He has provided information about the number of pens, the information to be printed on them, and the delivery location.
2. Needed information:
   a. Pen style
   b. Ink color
   c. Pen casing color
   d. Print color and style
   e. Date and time needed

3. If his phone number is in the letterhead, phoning is an option; otherwise, writing is the only choice.

4. Phoning would create greater goodwill for the company. A call is faster and more personal.

## Checkpoint 3-5

Sample response: Reference manuals are resources for those who write or prepare messages. Writers may view reference manuals as "style" or "how to" books. Most manuals contain information about grammar, punctuation, capitalization, abbreviations, word division, numbers, symbols, and proofreading. Some manuals also have sections devoted to technology, filing, and getting a job.

## Checkpoint 3-6

1. Respond by saying that using both pronouns—regardless of which is listed first—shows more gender neutrality than using only one.

2. In long documents where both masculine and feminine pronouns are used, a writer can switch the pronoun that is used first—him/her, her/him; she/he, he/she.

# CHAPTER 4

## Checkpoint 4-1

1. A vertical list helps readers:

   a. Focus their attention on what the writer thinks is important.

   b. Organize their responses, if a reply is needed.

   c. Find particular items if they need to refer to the message more than once.

2. A vertical list helps writers:

   a. Draw attention to specific items in a message.

   b. Be sure all important items have been included.

   c. Make it easier for the reader to respond.

## Checkpoint 4-2

Sample response: Please send a Model 56A CD player to replace the one that arrived in damaged condition.

## Checkpoint 4-3

Advise Jordan to describe the problem calmly and clearly—and furnish documentation of his purchase. He might also ask for instructions on how to return the damaged player.

# Checkpoint 4-4

Sample response: Because the CD player is a gift for my sister's birthday, I would appreciate receiving a replacement unit by June 12.

# Checkpoint 4-5

Sample response: The 100 dozen pink sweetheart roses ordered on January 12 will be shipped February 9. Thank you for the confidence you have shown in us by placing this order.

# CHAPTER 5

## Checkpoint 5-1

1. Weak. It doesn't introduce the topic of the message.
2. Weak. It gives the bad news before the explanation.
3. Weak. It avoids the topic of the message.
4. Weak. The reader might believe the repairs will be free.

## Checkpoint 5-2

1. Readers will benefit because colleagues and customers will be able to enter the building more easily.
2. Readers benefit because they know the company is concerned about protecting its employees and/or clients and respects their right to privacy.

## Checkpoint 5-3

In these examples, the implied bad news is more concise.

## Checkpoint 5-4

1. Weak. It suggests the problem will occur again.
2. Strong. It refers to a counterproposal and makes action easy.
3. Weak. It doesn't relate to the topic of the message.
4. Weak. It refers to the bad news.

## Checkpoint 5-5

Sample response: Pam, you have every reason to believe your performance review will be positive. Your work reflects skill and creativity.

(The close might be "I'm looking forward to meeting with you in July.")

## Checkpoint 5-6

1. The reader would probably react positively. He or she could expect that an adjustment will be made because the problem was caused by a manufacturing problem rather than a use problem.

2. The reaction could be neutral because the subject line doesn't say whether an adjustment will be made.

3. The reader would probably react neutrally. The subject line refers to the topic without giving a clue about whether the claim will be adjusted.

4. The reaction would probably be positive; the subject line leads the reader to believe an adjustment will be made.

# CHAPTER 6

## Checkpoint 6-1

1. a. carpet cleaning/homeowner—prolong carpet life; easier than doing it by themselves

   b. changing location of supply cabinet/office supervisor—more centrally located; more room to access contents

   c. computer/insurance agent—potential for Internet access and e-mail communication with clients; improved record keeping and billing potential; better client service

   d. stapler/office worker—safety; convenience

   e. tax preparation/sales associate—accuracy; familiarity with changes in law

2. Sample response for b: Productivity can be increased by moving the supply cabinet to the west wall, adjacent to the file cabinets.

## Checkpoint 6-2

1. Number of people who attended last year's show.
   Number of people who stopped at your booth.
   Number of new customers generated as a result of displaying at the show.
   Dollars of revenue generated from new customer accounts.

2. Compare the revenue generated from this event with the revenue generated from other forms of advertising; say what previously used form of advertising you will eliminate and why. Remind your supervisor that the larger space will allow you to display more of your products.

3. No. In fact, the writer might ask for a response well before the registration deadline to be sure the company gets a prime location.

# Checkpoint 6-3

Sample responses:

| | |
|---|---|
| Title: | Improved Attendance Leads to Improved Service |
| Problem Statement: | During the past six months, 38 percent of our service staff failed to meet their scheduled work commitment at least once; 28 percent failed to meet the schedule two or more times. |
| Objective: | Reduce staff absences by half within the next six months. |
| Methods/ Activities: | Review materials provided by National Restaurant Association.<br>Interview workers who have not met their schedule.<br>Poll all staff regarding their shift preferences and availability.<br>Develop plan to reward those who meet schedule (e.g. first opportunity for overtime or holiday release).<br>Review selection criteria used in hiring; modify based on interview results.<br>Prepare and implement revised schedule. |
| Evaluation: | Monitor attendance and calculate absence rate. |

# CHAPTER 7

## Checkpoint 7-1

1. The objective is weak because it is so general.

2. The objective is fairly strong. It mentions the type of institution in which the applicant wishes to work and specifies the geographic location. The objective could be made stronger by including statements about advancement opportunities or a specific area such as accounting.

3. The objective is strong. It mentions the type of position desired and some of the skills the applicant would bring to the position. In addition, it expresses the desire for advancement.

## Checkpoint 7-2

Sample response:

Dear Mrs. Wilson:

Your presentation to WTC's retail management class last spring inspired me to pursue a career in fashion merchandising, and an internship at The Petite Lady would be an excellent start. Please accept this letter as my application for such a position.

## Checkpoint 7-3

In most circumstances, it would not be appropriate for a worker to use an employer's stationery for a letter of application. Letterhead stationery should be reserved for company-related business, and a worker's search for employment generally does not meet that criterion. To use an employer's stationery for this purpose would be unethical and could make a terrible impression on the prospective employer.

## Checkpoint 7-4

An employee: receiving a promotion; winning a contest; becoming a parent . . .

A customer: receiving a community service award; winning a sales promotion; completing a business expansion . . .

A colleague: being elected to office in an organization; becoming a parent; retiring; receiving a promotion . . .

## Checkpoint 7-5

Because not all workers may celebrate the Christmas season, you might advise your employer to send a Happy New Year message or one with an end-of-year good wishes theme. A Christmas message phrased as an invitation to share the spirit of the season with those who celebrate it might also be appropriate.

*Checkpoint Solutions*

# INDEX